RSA

Exam Practice

TYPEWRITING SKILLS
STAGE III

HEINEMANN
EDUCATIONAL

in association with the RSA Examinations Board

Heinemann Educational,
a division of Heinemann Educational Books Ltd,
Halley Court, Jordan Hill, Oxford OX2 8EJ

OXFORD   LONDON   EDINBURGH
MELBOURNE   SYDNEY   AUCKLAND
IBADAN   NAIROBI   GABORONE   HARARE
KINGSTON   PORTSMOUTH NH (USA)
SINGAPORE   MADRID

First published 1989
Reprinted 1989

British Library Cataloguing in Publication Data
Typewriting skills.
Stage 3.
1. Typing – Manuals
I. Title   II. Series
652.3

ISBN 0-435-45152-9

Produced by DMD, Oxford
Printed by Thomson Litho Ltd, East Kilbride, Scotland

Contents

Stationery

In exams you will be handed a folder (Answer Book) containing stationery for your use during the exam.

The letterhead has details of a fictitious organisation, Praxiteles Group, with the address Praxiteles House, Adam Street, London WC2N 6EZ.

In Part 1 exams you will receive

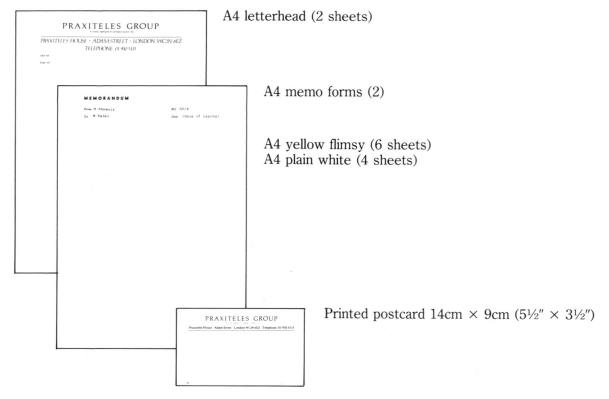

A4 letterhead (2 sheets)

A4 memo forms (2)

A4 yellow flimsy (6 sheets)
A4 plain white (4 sheets)

Printed postcard 14cm × 9cm (5½″ × 3½″)

In Part 2 exams you will receive plain white paper: 6 sheets A4 and 2 sheets A5.
(See also note on page 1 – Introduction)

Introduction

This book provides practice in the types of task included in RSA Stage III Typewriting Skills examinations and the keying-in tasks in Stage III Word Processing examinations. The material has been specially compiled by a group of Chief Examiners currently involved in these examinations.

RSA Examinations Board records its thanks to Margaret Rees-Boughton, Consultant to RSA for Office Subjects, for her work in the origination of the book and in editing it, and to the following Chief Examiners:

Phillip Arnold   Margaret Reid
Sue Fox   and
Tessa Greig   Gill Stoker

Worked examples

Worked examples are provided so that you can *check*:
● that you have accurately interpreted handwriting
● you have correctly followed instructions given in the drafts
● accuracy of your typed text, and correct any keyboarding errors.
There are many options in regard to details of display, such as the number of clear line spaces you choose to leave between items. The worked examples are intended to illustrate possible ways to present tasks and in matters of such detail should not be interpreted as the only acceptable version(s).

NB: In exams, you must always leave a left margin (at least half-inch). It may not always have been possible to show this in the printed worked examples.

Stationery

The RSA exam letterhead, memo and postcard suitable for use with the exercises in this book are available from bookshops (see previous page). If you should experience any difficulty in buying the Stationery Pad, then contact the Publishers.

RSA Exam Practice

This book is one of a series in which RSA provides practice material based on the types of task set in RSA exams in Typewriting Skills (and the keying-in tasks in Word Processing exams).

In some tasks – especially for Part 2 – the work may be more demanding than that in the exam. This will help you to develop confidence in your ability to cope calmly in the exam with problems that at first sight *may* look forbiddingly complicated.

PRACTICE FOR PART 1 EXAMS

Notes to candidates

Any or all of the drafts in Part 1 exams will include:
- words shortened which you must type in full with correct spelling
- deliberate errors in spelling of words in general use
- deliberate errors of agreement. That is, two words within a sentence may be in different tenses eg 'We *did wanted* to go there tomorrow' or a mixture of plural and singular eg 'The *sisters has* good qualifications'.

Letters and memos

In the exam one copy is required of both the letter and the memo. In addition, you will be instructed to take an extra carbon copy (that is, two carbon copies) of *either* the letter *or* the memo. Details of the extra copy's destination will be included in the wording of the task and you may type them on the top copy (original); these details *must* be typed on the carbon copy to go to the extra addressee, and on the copy which would be filed. On one of the carbon copies, destination details must be highlighted (eg ticked or underlined) to route it to the extra addressee.

Any errors (including overtyping) left uncorrected in carbon copies will be penalized.

If you do not produce all tasks including carbon copies, you cannot pass the exam.

Aim to type, check and correct letter, memo and copies within 30 minutes

30.00

Postcards

In the exam and in this book drafts requiring postcards lack one detail. This is typical of office work: it is not always possible to wait until every detail is available before issuing work.

About 20 minutes after the start of the exam the invigilator will stop candidates working so that all can hear and make a written note of the missing detail which will then be announced. For the purpose of providing such an interruption when you are using this book, a note of where this extra detail can be found is given with each postcard exercise.

Aim to type, check and correct a postcard within 5 minutes

05.00

Typed drafts for correction

In addition to deliberate errors in spelling and errors of agreement, these drafts include typing errors for you to spot and correct.

You will need to use one or more continuation sheets which must be numbered. There is no rule stating where page numbers must be positioned, but it is of course important that whether at top or bottom of the page the number is separated from the main body of text so that it can be clearly and easily seen.

Aim to type, check and correct this type of task within 35 minutes

35.00

Task 1.1

Date

Typist: Take an extra copy of this letter, please (in addition to the one on yellow paper)

CONFIDENTIAL

Mr S Quinton
West Wing
Beech House
Church Lane
SOUTH OCKENDEN
Essex RM15 4EJ

Ref SO/4/HP

Dr Mr Quinton

Following my recent visit to discuss your present plans, I now advice you that, on receipt of your authorisation, work could start on Thurs of next week, (typist-please give date) *3 October* + wd be completed in time for your wife's birthday, ie within two weeks' of commencement.

xxxxx As discussed w you, the "Domed Regent" summer chalet will be erected at the site marked on the enclosed sketch map.

A firm concrete base will first be laid, topped with quarry tiles and having two curved, shallow steps to the level of the lawn. *and having a yorkstone paved surround*

A shaped pond, approx 2m x 4 metres with a maximum depth of 60 cm, will also be made as marked on *show* the sketch map.

As requested by you, I enclose an extra copy of this letter (together with an additional copy of the map) for your co-owner, Mr Shaw.

My co has plenty of exp in projects of this nature. ~~To allay your fears about the integration of the chalet,~~ I can assure you that the necy work will be carried out with

4

as little incon as possible by a group of resp workers. // I look forward to hearing from you within the next few days.

Yrs sinc
PRAXITELES LANDSCAPES   PLC

_____

H Phoenix   Enc.
Director   cc Mr Shaw
_____

(Memo) to M Patel   from H Phoenix   Ref 50/4

PROPOSED WORK AT BEECH HOUSE, SOUTH OCKENDEN

I have today written to Mr Quinton confirming that this work could be put in hand immediately. (This project is apparently a surprise birthday gift for his wife and ~~who has been a good customer in the past~~ I have made a def promise ~~to complete~~ to start as soon as we receive his confirmation and to complete in two weeks.) The work has also been agreed with the co-owner, Mr _____

In the meantime, please check with the mfr that the chalet wl be delivered here during next week. This was discuss with their salesman yesterday. [Please detail the quantities of materials needed + cheque there is suff in stock. I have ordered 12 shrubs, (forty water plants) and (36 alpines.)
(who has worked at Beech House before)

The best team wd be George, Tom and Ali (I think). Perhaps you could (let me know if there are any difficulties) then (check their schedules.)

Task 1.2

Please type a letter to Mr F Latham of
2 Queens Dr, Manchester M24 4EQ
our ref MW/JK/1

Dr Mr Latham

LEATHER COAT

I have now had an opp to consider the report recd from our ~~recved~~ received
~~The evidence has now been recd from the evidence recd~~
laboratory ∧ about yr leather coat. // It is necy to ~~carry out~~ follow special
procedures when cleaning such coats & ~~in accordance~~
~~with company policy~~ our manager was correct to
estimate ~~$~~ 3 weeks.

(The co therefore accepts that you shd not have had
to wait for yr coat. // With regard to yr complaint
(for 7 weeks) ~~that the cleaning of the coat was very poor~~ about
the quality of cleaning, I feel that the manager
was justified in asking you to pay £12 for the
extra cleaning to remove ~~oily patches down~~ stubborn stains. Our
gntee (only) normal soiling (covers) and yr coat
was heavily soiled down the front.

In addition, the laboratories report includes
the following wording:
        "It is clear that solvents were used
        prior to specialised cleaning & this
        has left (faded & rubbed) patches
        down the front of the coat. ∧ Dirty This is against the advise of the mfrs.
        marks on left sleeve are paint
        marks & will not come out."

In view of the fact that yr coat was
kept for to long a time, the company is willing to
offer a reduction of five pounds. This will compensate
for the incon suffer by you. I cannot accept resp

for the damage caused by solvents.

I look forward to hearing from you.

yrs scly

M Winston
Director

Memo from M Winston, Director to E Hayes, Branch Manager (Manchester). Ref as letter. Mark it CONFIDENTIAL and please take an extra copy.

I enclose a laboratory report on the leather coat from yr branch. They bel we are not to blame for faulty cleaning but in future there must always be ~~12 members of staff in the dept~~ enough staff on duty to avoid delays.

I sh be in the north west on Thurs and Fri of next week to see Janet Baimer & I am sending her a copy of this memo to remind her of our meeting at 2 pm on Thursday Typist: give date of Thurs of next week). We could all have dinner that evening at 1930 if you are agreeable. We could then discuss fully the problems we are having with leather & sheepskin cleaning. Obviously staff are not taking enough care and it may mean that you and Janet will has to consider re-training and/or disciplinary measures for some. The branch image must not suffer.

Task 1.3

The Manager
Woodbridge Hotel
Wallman Street
IPSWICH Suffolk
IP2 3GW   Ref PGC/SS

Dr Sir

PRAXITELES   GROUP CONFERENCE

An unexpected problem has arisen in connection w my co's
conference, due to be held at your hotel in a fortnight's
time. One of our main speakers, Mr Alec Jones, due to be
present for the whole 4 days, has ~~been asked if he may~~ been involved in an accident
and now needs to bring with him his wife and daughters,
aged ~~ten~~ 10 and 12.   preferably in a room with 2 beds

I presume it will be possible for Mr + Mrs Jones to share a
double room. Are you able also to offer accomm to the 2
young girls? Mrs Jones and the children will also require
~~evening meals~~ and ~~breakfast~~. Meals will be taken with the
~~remainder of the~~ conference delegates. If this is possible, please
advise me immed. I am sending a copy of this letter to
Mr Jones, who will be personally resp for the extra exp involved expenses?
+ shd be invoiced accordingly. // I confirm that the total
number of "live-in" delegates, including Mr Jones, remains at
26. In addition, there will be 8 daily visitors, needing
~~afternoon tea~~ and morning ~~coffee~~ drinks and lunch on each day of the
conference.

All other arrangements, use of rooms and
facilities etc, remain as agreed with you.

                        conference cat
A copy of our ~~programme for the conference~~ is now enclosed.
May I take this opp to thank you for your help in the

Typist: you'll need an extra copy of this letter + one ~~yellow~~ paper please.

past, and hope that this late change will not prove incon. As arranged, I will call to see you between 2.30 ~~1430~~ and ~~1500~~ ~~3.00~~ hours on Fri of next week (typist: insert date).   4 October 199_

yrs fflly

Conference Secretary
Enc.

(Memo) to Alec Jones from Sheila Suzman Ref SS/218

PERSONAL

Praxiteles Group Conference

Enclosed is a copy of a letter wh has today been sending to the W— Hotel.

I do not anticipate any difficulties regarding the accommodation of your wife and daughter's. We greatly appreciate yr decision to attend the conference despite the accident and ~~although you are technically responsible for the~~ costs incurred by your family the Accountant has therefore been instructed to make an ex gratia payment. Please send him a photocopy of the receipted a/c in due coarse. (to cover your family's hotel expenses)

                    full and
I wishes you a/ speedy recovery.

9

Letters and memos

Please send the following letter to Mrs D Williams, 3 Rutland Cres, WARRINGTON WA1 3EY & mark it PERSONAL. Take an extra carbon copy, inc. one on yellow paper.

Our
Ref F4.3.2 ← Date
PERSONAL

Dr Mrs Williams

THE OWLS NEST, WARRINGTON

Typist: No apostrophe in Owls Nest

As requested, I enclosed our estimate for the ~~full range of kitchen furniture~~ fittings you are considering for yr ~~new~~ restaurant and ~~new accom~~. [These fittings have been chosen from the point of view of: their providing

a) a clear sweep of working surfaces
b) hygienically sealed work tops
c) adequate storage space ~~& freezing capacity for yr frozen foods~~.

The designs has been
~~Our designers have~~ chosen in order to give efficient food production where (the min of exp cleanliness and speed,) are important.

The prices quoted are competitive + we have allowed
~~We consider that are much lower than~~ those have allowed for expansion as yr bus grows.
business

Our usual terms will apply, ie a trade discount of 5 per cent, and a cash discount of 10% if the a/c is settled within 28 days. [Mr Appleton, our regional sales manager, wl be in yr area on Wed Typist: it's the first Wed of next month & I am sending him a copy of this letter so that he can arrange to call & see you.

2 October 19—

I hope by that time (yr partner & you) wl be able to give him a decision

If there is any way in wh I can help

you, please do not hesitate to contact me.

yrs scly

John Millward

Manager

enc

CC Mr Appleton.

Memo from John Millward, Manager to Ronald Appleton, Regional Sales Manager. Ref FW.3.1

I am enclosing a copy of a letter I have sent to Mrs D W— of Warrington. I recd an enquiry from her for misc fixtures & fittings for the new restaurant she is opening in approx 3 months.

I will not have an opp to see her ~~because I have a very heavy schedule over the next 3 months~~ because of my commitments. I thought that you cd give her some advise on the following lines.

Other mfrs do not offer the range of colours that we offer — this is most important! Our joiners are highly trained craftsmen who are able to fit awkward areas to the best advantage.

Please call to see me when you are here on Friday. I am free between 10 am & 11 am & again 1500 to 1600 hours. It would appear that concern is being expressed about the decreasing number of 'domestic' kitchens we are fitting. High interest rates, do you think? Or is there some other reason?

(Memo) from Lynn Marsh, Personnel Officer
to Eden Poulet, Fieldwork Section   Ref R28946

(Extra copy on yellow paper)

Of the 6 candidates interviewed for the 2 clerical posts for Fieldwork Section, four wd def be suitable for employment here.

I have therefore chosen those most fitted for your section & retained the other 2 names on our books (though at this stage with no gntee of jobs). ~~I give below details of the~~ The following have been offered employment with you. ~~new employees in your division.~~

MR RICHARD PHILPOT, aged 18, a post 'A' level school leaver whose home is in Kent.

MISS MARIE MANUEL, aged 21, currently a junior clerk with a rival finance company, who lives in Essex.

The appointments will take affect from the beginning of next month ~~so you may expect~~. Both candidates have been ~~told~~ ask* to report direct to you. [I am sending a copy of this memo to the Training Officer, since (training and induction) of these new clerks will take plaice as soon as he is able to arrange it. The Training Officer will notify ~~inform~~ you when a suitable opp arises.// I bel both these young people wl settle well + work effectively, ~~but~~ please let me know immed if there are any problems.

PERSONAL   Ref R28 946/LM

Mr Richard Philpot
82 Dunbar St
ORPINGTON Kent
BR5 8CF

Dr Mr Philpot

APPOINTMENT OF CLERICAL OFFICER

Following your ~~application and recent~~ interview, I am pleased to
offer you the ~~post employment~~ post of Grade 3 Clerical Officer in the
Fieldwork Section of this company.

Your appt will take effect from Mon (typist please give date —
8 October 1991 first Mon of next month) and you shd report at 0900 hours
to Mr E Paulet in Fieldwork Section on the 4th floor of
this building.

You are required to work a minimum of 35 hours per week.
The company operates a flexitime system but you must be at
work between 1000 hours and 4 pm. 1600

You will be entitled to 24 day*'s leave each year, ~~leave
for this year will be calculated on a pro rata basis~~. Your
commencing salary will be at Grade 3 on scale point 2.
A list of salary scales are in the introductory booklet
enclosed with this letter. (the satisfactory completion of)

Your appointment is subject to the enclosed medical statement +if
necy you will be required to undergo a medical examination.

We hope you will dev + enjoy your career with us.

Yrs sinc

Mrs Lynn Marsh, Personnel Officer

Encs

Letters and memos

CONFIDENTIAL
Mr J F Slaid
Adelphi Engineering
Sussex Rd
LONDON WC2N 3AB

Mark this letter CONFIDENTIAL
Extra copy needed - one on
yellow paper please.

Our ref M183.4
Yours JFS/PB
24 Sept 1991

Dr James
Thank you for your letter of yesterday's date. I sugget we meet for lunch on Thurs of next week (give date) at 1230 hours followed by a formal meeting here at approx 1400 hours. 2 pm.

May I say that I shares your hope that we can reach a def agreement on future supplies of raw materials being ordered jointly by our two firms. [My ~~directors~~ partners agree ~~have agreed~~ that both cos ordering together would be better ~~more likely~~ able to reap the benefit of larger discounts that bulk buying will produce. As we are, so to speak, next-door neighbours there should be few problems with inward delivery and breaking bulk.]

*Damon Sangay, my Chief Buyer, ~~too been invited~~ as I have asked him to be present at our discussions after lunch. His previous exp with co-operative buying shd prove invaluable in our deliberations. // I look foreword to a profitable meeting.

yours sinc

I am sending a copy of this letter to

H Romano
Managing Director
cc Damon Sangay
file.

14

(Memo)

TO Damon Sangay from Henry Romano Ref AE/HR

<u>Joint Buying – Adelphi Engineering</u>

I enclose a copy of my letter to James Slaid, Director of Adelphi Engineering, w whom negotiations have now been opened to decide the feasibility of joint bulk buying of raw materials.

As stated in the letter, I should like you to be present at next weeks' meeting, which wl start at (give time) hours. In the meantime would you consider the following points.

If a monthly order of, say, £5,000 were placed with the mfr would the discounts (now 2%, then 5 per cent) outweigh the exp of braking bulk and onward delivery?

What specific problems wd be likely in regard to delivery, storage, etc, and how could they be successfully overcome?

~~In the case of faulty materials being used~~, Can you recom a reliable division of responsibility for orders, particularly in the case of faulty goods being recd, (other problems or delayed delivery?

It might be a good idea for us to talk ~~I think you and I should meet together~~ prior to the meeting at, say, 1000 hours in my office on that Thursday. Please let me know if this is incon for you ~~and we will set another time.~~

I need hardly say that I greatly values your help and initiative in this matter.

2 Postcards

REDBRIDGE PERSONAL COMPUTER CLUB

Mrs Doreen Foster
19 Western Approach
Seven Kings
ILFORD   Essex
IG8 4BT

Date as Postmark

Mr B S Spiro
Praxiteles Group
Praxiteles House
Adam Street
LONDON   WC2N 6EZ

Dear Mr Spiro

I note from our previous correspondence that you have kindly agreed
to address our Annual General Meeting on the subject of "Software
Applications for the Home Computer User". The members of this group
are looking forward to meeting you and I now enclose some travel
directions. The meeting will take place at Jubilee Hall, Claremont
Avenue, Ilford, on the first Monday of next month.

The business part of the meeting will start at 1930 hours and there
will be a short break for refreshments before your address, which is
expected to commence at about 2030 hours. We hope, however, that you
will join us for the entire evening.

Would you please confirm as soon as possible that you are able to
keep this appointment?

Yours sincerely

Doreen Foster

Doreen Foster
Club Secretary

Send a postcard to Mrs Foster — date it today please:

*Thank you for your reminder about the Personal Computer
Club's Annual General Meeting. I am happy to confirm that
I am looking forward to the event and I shall be able to
attend for the whole evening. As I have a late afternoon
meeting here, I shall come straight from the office + expect
to arrive at Ilford Station at .. hours. I would appreciate
it if someone could meet me there. If this is
~~not possible,~~ I will of course pick up a taxi.*

For extra detail
see page 29

16

Task 2.2

Paperback Book Department
PRAXI BOOKS
8 Adam Street, London WC2N 6EZ

A division of the **Praxiteles** Group

Barclay/Access No

_____

ADVICE NOTE

PLEASE PRESENT THIS FORM WHEN YOU CALL

Mr	B	Sheldon
10 Regency Road		
Harborne		
BIRMINGHAM		B17 12QQ
Tel No (Home) 021 428 9786		
(Business) 021 400 1717		
Office use only	Advise	Phone
	(Post)	

Category	Fiction	Ref BX43
Date	14 October	
Author	Sheila Barnard	
Title	The Retaliation of Edwina – Volume 3: The Matriarch of Dalgety Minories	
ISBN	0-330-290752-Q	

Publishers: Criterion Books

~~We have pleasure in advising you that the above order has been received and will be reserved for you.~~*

Out of stock – customer advised*

* Delete as appropriate

(Please send a postcard to Mr B Sheldon. Date the card for today.)

Date

We regret to inform you that "The R_____ of E_____ – Volume 3: The M_____ of D_____ M_____" ordered on 14 October last is out of print. The publishers inform us that a reprinting will commence on the 1st of next month. Copies should be available within ~~8 weeks~~ ~~2 months~~ from then. Please inform us if you wish to cancel the order in which event your deposit of _____ will be refunded.

For extra detail see page 29

£2.00.

17

Task 2.3

BEAUCHAMP, HETHERSETT & SONS PLC
5th Floor Homerton House
Ward Business Park
Thurrock Road
CHELMSFORD
Essex   CM1 3AB

The Sales Manager
Praxiteles Group
Praxiteles House
Adam Street
LONDON   WC2N 6EZ

Dear Sir

Proposed Office Refurbishment

My firm has recently moved into new premises and although the building
itself is modern and comfortable, the decor and furniture leave a great
deal to be desired. My Board has therefore decided to embark upon the
complete refurbishment of these offices.

We have been looking with interest at your catalogue and it would appear
that the "Premier" range of pine and grey furniture may best suit our
requirements. We note that you offer to arrange an advisory visit and
would like to avail ourselves of this service. I am therefore writing
to request such a visit as soon as possible.

Yours faithfully

Richard Dereham

Richard Dereham
Office Administrator

Send a pc to the Office Administrator – do not insert date.

Thank you for your enquiry regarding the refurbishment of your
offices. Our representative, Mr John Beeston, will be visiting
your area in the next ~~few weeks~~ ~~two months~~. He could call on you ✗
to consider your exact requirements and would bring with
him samples of colours, finishes, etc. He will also be able
to tell you about our brand new furniture range (not yet
in the catalogue) and our special discount offers. Please
telephone Mr Beeston on 01 930 5115 Extension ... to make   128
a definite appointment. He will be expecting your call.

**For extra detail
see page 29**   128

18

```
Praxiteles Records
Classical Music Department

Customer Orders

Miss J Leggett, Flat 2, No 8 Edwarde Court,
Hagley Road, Edgbaston, BIRMINGHAM B16 8PQ
Miaskovsky Piano Sonatas        Olympia
Cat No OCD214

Mr Martin Bell, 37 Oakland Drive,
Edgbaston, BIRMINGHAM B16 4LW
Rossini: The Barber of Seville    EMI
Cat No CDS7470348

Miss E Wortley, 44 Garden Road,
Harborne, BIRMINGHAM B19 6RR
Wagner: The Valkyrie             EMI
Cat No CDS749534

Mr D Harris, Hendon House, Middle Green,
nr WORCESTER, WR17 8PP
Tchaikovsky: Eugene Onegin        Decca
Cat No 417413-2

Mr B Sheldon, 10 Regency Road,
Harborne, BIRMINGHAM B17 12QQ
Beethoven Symphonies 1 & 7        EMI
Cat No CDC749622

Mr D Stevens, Anderson House, Gilhurston
Road, Quinton, BIRMINGHAM B19 6PN
Mozart: The Marriage of Figaro  Decca
Cat No 421333-1
```

Send a pc to Mr Martin Bell

P_____ R_____
C_____ M____ D_____

Today's Date

Rossini : The Barber of Seville
We have pleasure in advising you that
the above recording which you asked us to
order on your behalf is now in stock and
will be held for you for ~~2 weeks~~ ~~10 days~~ subsequent
to which it will be added to our sales stocks
if not collected by you. The price is £22.99.
Please quote R/SHE/1288 in any communication.

For extra detail see page 29

£22.99

Postcards

TELEPHONE CALL FOR   Colin Westmorland

FROM	TAKEN BY	Jane Springett
Mrs M Edmunds 28 Camberley Drive REIGATE Surrey RH2 8BW	TIME	0920 hours

MESSAGE

KITCHEN PLANNING AND INSTALLATION SERVICE

Mrs Edmunds telephoned this morning in response to the article in "Homes". She already has our brochure. Mrs Edmunds is particularly interested in the solid oak "Master" range of fitments and also requires a coloured two-and-a-half bowled sink unit, with waste disposal. She wants all new appliances - oven, hob, dishwasher, washing machine, refrigerator, microwave - built in as far as possible. The kitchen is said to be 8' 6" x 19' 0" and forms part of a new extension which is now nearing completion. Advice is also sought regarding wall tiling, floor covering, lighting and colour schemes. It is important that installation should start as soon as the building work is finished.

Could you arrange to visit in the near future, please?

Typist: send a p c to Mrs Edmunds - date today

☑ Thank you for your telephone ~~request~~ ~~enquiry for~~ our kitchen service. Our local surveyor, Mr Colin Westmorland, will call in the next few days to draw up a scale plan to your exact requirements & arrange a convenient commencing date. Please telephone him on 0278 63910 for a definite appointment. Meanwhile, you may like to visit your nearest local showroom at - to view our extensive range of cabinets and appliances.

Leatherhead.
(date)

For extra detail see page 29

20

Task 2.6

MEMORANDUM

From	MRD	*Ref*	MRD/pa
To	P Matthews	*Date*	

Harringdon Green Up Scheme

I have contacted the members of the Harringdon Society in connection with setting up an allocation list for the Green Up Scheme. We have now agreed the following.

Area	Members responsible
Princess Corner triangle	Mary Bishop, Kevin Walker, John Cunningham
Rosa Road border	Terry O'Neill, Joan Barstow, Josephine Sutherland
Barnett Hill corner	Connie Cooper, Bella Evans, Jack Wright, Walter Mason
Mason Hall corner	Barbara Morris, Trudie Bristow, Peter Miles, Carolyn Blake
Redmond Road entry	Evelyn Silver, Mary Tomlinson, Geoffrey Leo, Malcolm Morse

Details of dates and times will be forwarded later, and progress reports will be sent to you at regular intervals.

Send a pc to: Barbara Morris, 3 The Limes, Oakwood, Harringdon, BOURNEMOUTH, Dorset BH62 4QP

Today's date

We have now completed the list for the H_____ G___ U_ S_____ and you are part of the team that will tackle M_____ H_ c_____. Please let me know if you are interested in being ~~Committee Chairperson~~ ~~Scheme Chairman~~ in the next session — I should be grateful if you could get back to me as soon as possible on this. Contact me on my home telephone number which is 0202 683090

mRD

For extra detail see page 29

Task 3.1

spaced caps

/// ///spaces when spaced caps.

PRAXITILE PRODUCTS LTD ← *spaced caps*

type in 1½ or double spacing, except for section 2, which should be typed in single spacing

change to double → after type. let head (TU2) twice (4 spaces)

double

Over the past few months we have been reassessing the design concepts of our products. Extensive market reserach has been carried out with householders ~~in a number of towns and cities~~ in all parts of the country. This has confirmed the suspicion that our tile designs are lagging behind the times, and that drastic measures must be taken in order to bring ourselves back in to line with current trends.

shd def be

leave 4 clear line spaces here

return to single then return to double

The following tile products ~~are being~~ redesigned.

– in double.

(1) Ceramic wall tiles ← *shoulder head TU1 here*

These tiles are suitable for use in kitchens and bathrooms. An attractive flowers and fruit design in a variety of colour combinations has been selected for kitchens, with matching plain tiles to provide for greater flexibility of layout. For teh bathroom we have chosen a simple, three-colour yacht design. ~~Wavy blue lines~~

(red, yellow and orange are the colours we recom)

A wavy blue sea motif ~~representing the sea~~ are chosen for the accompanying plain tiles which, like the kitchen version, may be used in varying combinations with the yacht design. The motif tiles will be sold in packs of ten, and the plain tiles in packs of twenty.

~~We shall not be able to supply in quantities smaller~~

double

(2) Self-adhesive floor tiles ← *TU2 (1 clear line space)*

This is a product line which has been steadily growing in popularity. A number of different designs have been selected, which should provide ~~the customer with~~ an attractive choice of styles. The following product names have been suggested, and are to be finalised once market research results have been received.

(a) Italian Renaissance

(b) Celtic

(c) Gothic

(d) 4. Georgian

(e) 5. Victorian

(f) (6) Edwardian

TU2

just

A new, hard-wearing plastic has recently been developed. This is virtually unbreakable, and will soon be introduced into the manufacture of these new floor tiles. They will be self-adhesive,

single line spacing

single line SP

with a peel-off backing, ~~and this should make them easy to cut~~ *wh wl facilitate cutting* into shape if necessary before laying. They will be sold in packs of ten.

X ← *double & TU 2*
X

(3) xx <u>Polystyrene ceiling tiles</u> ← *TU 1 (shoulder heading)*

Instead of the completely plain surface of our present tiles, the new version will have a raised pattern. Up to six designs are planned, ~~including honeycomb, striped, checked and wavy.~~ *As in the case of the floor tiles, we bel* They will be sold in packs of ten. A special glue is being obtained form a top manufacturer, to be given away with quantity purchases as part of a promotional campaign.

leave 6 clear line spaces here   *single now & TU*

(4) xx <u>Marketing strategy</u> ← *back to double* ← *TU 1 (shoulder head)*

We are now compiling a comprehensive book of samples for sales staff to show to suppliers. There will also be a brief question-naire ~~for completion~~. In addition to these activities, a promotional exhibition evening is planned, to which all our major clinets will be invited.

leave 5 clear line spaces here   *back to single TU 6*   *return to double after this starting All sales*

All sales and marketing staff will be asked to attend a briefing meeting on this matter ~~very shortly~~. Please check the noticeboards regularly for further details.

this paragraph in caps, please

CAPS

Cont sheet
TU 4
Type '2'
TU 2
continue

(not need carbon copy for this)

(only ret 1 if in double line spacing)
for shoulder headings

35 minutes

Task 3.2

CAPS

Please type the following in double line spacing, except where indicated otherwise. Leave 5 clear line spaces at the points marked (x)

(capitals) House hunting? It is your first or perhaps you are in need of something larger ~~or more expensive~~. Whichever it is, you will probable need to raise a substantial loan. ~~Buying~~ a house will normally be the most expensive commodity you will ever buy, with a car def coming second.

There ~~is a restriction~~ are some necy constraints which you must consider when deciding on the house you like. You must obviously be able to afford the purchase price, but you are also responsible for such things as ~~rates and~~ maintenance~~, eg upkeep of the interior and exterior of the house~~. Once you are satisfied that you can fulfil these points, you can make a offer to the seller. * See below

Spaced caps

SOURCES OF MORTGAGE FUNDS (spaced capitals)

(x) 5 Clear line sp.

Type the following 3 numbered paragraphs in single line spacing, ensuring they are displayed consistently.

1 Building Societies TU6

Single

As a rule, building societies may be prepared to lend between 2½ and 3 times your ~~annual income~~ present salary. This will not normally be more than 95% of the surveyor's valuation of the property or the purchase price, whichever is the lower. Some building societies ~~will sometimes~~ have been known to consider percentages over 95%, but this depends to a large extent on the type of property and the particular building society involved. In addition, they will usually take into account both income of joint borrowers, or at least a proportion of the lower.

(x) ← TU6 Single

2 Banks and Other Lenders

Many lenders now provide funds on a similar basis to building societies. ~~The way in which they do this may~~ Their lending requirements wl sometimes differ from a building society, usually in the minimum amount they will lend. You need to find out as soon as you start house hunting the maximum amount you will be allowed to borrow. Some lenders now provide you with a certificate which confirms your borrowing level. / You should take great care in choosing your building society or other lender and find the one whose terms and conditions suit your requirements.

(x) TU 6 Single

3 Savings

No matter how much capital you need to borrow, you will be required to pay a deposit for your proprerty. You should, therefore, start a savings account with a bank or building society as soon as possible. This will not only help to accumulate money for your deposit, but will also improve your prospects of obtaining a mortgage.

Finally, on the lighter side, when you have bought your house, you will need to advise the following that you are moving

1 job related: employers, tax office

2 home based services: electricity and gas suppliers, milkman, newsagent, ~~rates office~~ district council

3 personal services: bank, doctor, dentist, insurance ~~- contents and other insurances~~ and credit card companies.

* You shd also advise yr solicitor. He will confirm the offer. If this is accepted, you must complete a loan application. The lender will then arrange for a co to survey the property and, if successful, you will receive an offer of loan.

don't spaced caps underline

LEGAL AID - IS THERE ANY JUSTICE?

General Notes For Applicants ← *spaced capitals not underlined*

leave 6 clear line spaces beneath this heading, and below each of the 2 lettered paragraph sections.

← TUT *single*

Your   *are likely to*

At some time in ~~everyone's~~ life you ~~will~~ need the services of a solicitor.
This may be for a conveyancing matter, making a will, or even a court case.
You may be entitled to legal aid. This is a Government scheme covering
the payment (or a proportion) of your solicitor's bill. Whether you pay
anything depends on your financial circumstances, ie:

(a)   your income
(b)   your martial status
(c)   your husband's/wife's income, if any
(d)   ~~how many children you have~~ *if you have children*
(e)   if you receive Supplementary Benefit.

Emergencies   TUT
~~What Happens To Your Application Form?~~

under lined   ~~Your~~ completed ~~from~~ will be sent to the relevant office. You can apply
for *emergency legal aid* This lasts only until a decision has been taken
on your full application. However, you must agree:

No clear linespace between these items

co-operate in any enquiry
(a)   to ~~give any assistance required~~ into your finanical position

NO SPACE

(b)   to pay any contribution that is decided

please type this paragraph in double line spacing

(c)   to pay the full cost of your case if it is found that you do not
      qualify for legal aid. ← TUT

* see below ← TUT

from
It costs nothing to ask for information on legal aid. This can be
a solicitor, ~~or an advice centre such as a Housing Advice Centre,~~ a
Citizens Advice Bureau, County or Magistrates' Court or a Public Library.
You will not qualify *then* if your earnings or savings are too high. It
only *helps* those who can least afford to pay for the help they need. No
have equal access
matter how little money you have, everyone should ~~be entitled~~ to justice.
in terms
Without this scheme, it would cost more ~~public money~~. There would be more
children in care, more people held in custody, or more Social Security
benefits for those unable to be awarded compensation for accidents.

double return Twice

← *double*

(✓)

single
What Happens If You Win (Or Lose)?

If you win, the amount you will have to pay your solicitor ~~and barrister~~
~~if you have one~~ will depend on whether the other side is ordered to pay
your costs and whether you are awarded anything. You may *by paid back*
some, or all, of any contribution you paid. When your ~~financial position~~
solicitor's costs
has been assessed, the balance is paid to you. // If you lose your case,
you will have to pay the maximum contribution which will have been worked
out when you made the application.

(✓)

To be typed in single linespacing

If your application is refused, you will rec a notice giving you an explanation. You can appeal against a refusal for legal reasons altho' not if the Department of ~~Health and~~ Social Security states that you are above the financial limit. You shd be told if you are entitled to appeal ~~and how to do it~~.

Applications Forms

These are obtainable from your local office of the Department of Social Security.
Complete and return your from as soon as possible.

Typed drafts for correction

PRAXI BOOKSHOPS LTD ← *(spaced capitals)*

Progress Report ← *(capitals)*

leave 7 linespaces clear here + at other points marked ↨

We have had a successful year on the whole. ~~There are several~~ *w a number of*
interesting developments.
~~changes to report.~~ These have included:

(a) the purchase of new premises
(b) special signings by celebrity authors
(3) cut-price books
(✓4) ~~cards and~~ stationery

and further details on these are given below.

New Premises

please type in double spacing, except for New Premises section, which should be typed in single spacing

The number of bookshops has increased from 20 ot 35 during the past
year. Premises have been purchased in cities such as Leeds, bristol
and Manchester, as well as in large towns and suburbs of London.
This has, of course, led to a dramatic increase in the number of
employees. Managers have been recruited for all our new shops, as
, both f/t & p/t
well as sales staff. Further acquisitions are envisaged for ~~the~~
the coming yr
~~future,~~ and for the first time we are extending our territory into
Scotland and Wales. ~~We are even considering a site in Paris.~~

Celebrity Signings

These have taken place in Central London and in Liverpool. Nine
authors in total have spent a busy afternoon talking to customers
and signing copies of their recently published books. They have
included:

1. Cranford Drumble - Little Old Ladies
2) Susan Eliot - Cooking For Your Freezer

(3) Richard Norris - <u>Diary Notes</u>

(4) (Going Home - Johnny Jones)

(5) Anita Glossop - <u>Derbyshire in Winter</u>

<u>Bargain Books</u>

These are high-quality remaindered books, always popular as
Christmas and birthday presents. ~~We are able to obtain them at
competitive prices.~~ They are displayed near the entrance to
each shop, and have been found to attract more customers, not
just to the Bargain Books section itself, but into all areas of
the shop. We estimate that this ~~has increased~~ *shd increase* turnover and
profits by up to 30 per cnet, thereby making it possible to
expand our business throughout the country.

<u>Greetings Cards and Stationery</u>

This has been an important additon to our business. Customers
come into a shop for a specific, ~~predetermined~~ purpose, and then
stay longer to browse. This can often lead to the purchase of
at least one book, as well as the item initially sought.// We
have found it best to position this section towards the rear of
the shop, so that customers have to pass rows of ~~attractively
presented~~ books on their way in and out. At the same time, a
window display makes it clear to passers-by that cards and
stationery is available.

Because of such rapid expansion, we feel it is now time to hold
a book shop managers' meeting. This is to take place within the
next few mnoths, and will be designed so that all managers can
meet and compare notes. *Co &* Directors will also attend.

Please type the following in single line spacing except where indicated otherwise and leave 3 clear line spaces before each of the 3 underlined headings.

HOW TO BECOME THE EXPERT HOME DECORATOR

Painting is an ~~easy and simple~~ *relatively easy* task, but it is important to plan the work to be undertaken. You need to spend time on preparing the surface properly before you start painting. If possible paint in good daylight. ~~- electric light may cast shadows and obscure any missed patches.~~ [It is definitely a] a good idea to decide on an order of painting, eg:

double line spacing

1 Ceilings   4 Windows
2 Walls   5 Radiators
3 Doors   6 Skirting Boards.

use capitals for these numbered items.

The info in this article include guidance on how to calculate quantities of materials, suggestions on tools you wl need, and a brief explanation on how to paint.

Calculating the quantity of paint you will need

DO NOT TYPE the diagram but leave 12 clear line spaces

To work out how much paint you will need to paint a room, measure the lenght of each surface and multiply by the height. This will give you the area in square metres. For emulsion - add all the wall and ceiling areas together to calculate the total surface area; for gloss - add all the metal and wood-work areas together. ~~Then refer to the chart at the back of the guide.~~ *Any Do-It-Yourself store will help you work out the quantities.*

Tools you are likely to need

Having the right tool for the right job will save time and effort. After completion, tools should be thoroughly cleaned; then they will stay in good
⊘ condition for longer. In order to do a professional job, you ~~will need~~ *require* the following *, although snd yr budget not allow you to purchase everything we recom, then you must ex your own judgement.*

please display lettered paragraphs us (a)
(a) Bucket, sponge, sugar soap, brush, stripper, step-ladder and dust sheets. It is necessary to wash paintwork and remove dust; a blow torch ~~and a~~ *or liquid* paint stripper is quick and efficient. Plastic sheets are better than newspapers for dust sheets, to avoid paint or water soaking through.

(b) Different size scrapers and various grades of sand paper. A wooden block is useful to hold the paper firmly. Wet-and-dry paper is excellent to achieve a smooth surface.

(c) Filler, filling knives and masking tape. Cracks have to be made good and masking tape is used to protect areas an edges not to be painted. ~~It is easy to peel off.~~

(d) Paint pad or roller, paint tray and brushes, depending on you prefer-ence. Paint pads or rollers are good for applying emulsion to larger areas. Brushes are necessary for finishing off and for applying gloss.

How to apply gloss or emulsion paints ~~using a brush~~

Make sure the brushes are clean and dry ~~and~~ *as well as* the surfaces to be painted. Dip up to one-third of the bristles in the paint. Hold the brush like a pen and if you are using gloss paint, do not brush out too thinly. Emulsion paint should be worked in with random strokes to cover evenly.

HAPPY DECORATING *spaced capitals*

PRACTICE FOR PART 2 EXAMS

Notes to candidates

Forms to be designed; straight-line charts/plans/diagrams

These tasks are designed to test your ability to allocate suitable space to headings within a form, and to plan the allocation of space to meet requirements for a chart/plan/diagram.

The chart etc will always require ruling, which you may produce by machine or by hand.

A word or phrase which occurs more than once throughout the two drafts will have to be changed by you to a different word/phrase given in the instructions.

Aim to type, check and correct two tasks (a form and a chart etc) within 35 minutes

> ### 35.00

Tables

In Stage III exams this type of task tests your ability to compile a table from information which is given to you. Drafts contain instructions on which information to include, what layout(s) to use, and the order(s) in which details are required eg alphabetically.

It is not always necessary to rule tables. In the exam, and when practising from this book, you should not waste time ruling when you are not specifically required to do so.

Aim to type, check and correct this type of task within 35 minutes

> ### 35.00

Postcard details

Task 2.1   The time of arrival at the station is 1905.
Task 2.2   The refund will be £2.00.
Task 2.3   The extension number is 128.
Task 2.4   The price is £22.99.
Task 2.5   The nearest local showroom is at Leatherhead.
Task 2.6   The telephone number is 0202 683090.

4 Forms and straight – line diagrams

Task 4.1 – form

PRAXI GLASS ~~CO~~ PLC

Typist: change Praxi Glass Co
to Praxi Glass PLC
in this notice & the plan

It will be necessary because of the building of
the new ~~office~~ block and canteen to mark out
a new parking ground. for staff This will be where
the old warehouse was and the police are
insistent that there should be no parking
~~in the streets nearby.~~ the side streets which surround this area. Special parking is to be
made available for ~~disabled employees who have~~ employees who have a disabled sticker.

You are asked to fill in and return the slip
below so that a suitable space can be allocated to ~~to staff~~
you. Before a special disc can be issued ~~to you~~
~~staff~~ will be asked to produce an owner's registration
document and a valid tax certificate.

Once the building is finish~~ed~~ and the workmen
have moved their huts, there will be ~~a~~ only limited
amount of ~~parking~~ space ~~only~~ on the ~~old~~ site.
This will ~~therefore~~ be left clear for fire access by
vehicles and ambulances.

PRAXI GLASS ~~CO~~ PLC

Typist: please draft a reply slip with
spaces for the following information

Surname   Forename(s)   Address

Department ~~and~~ position in the company

Telephone extension   Make of car   Registration

SDR.

PRAXI GLASS CO

PROPOSED PARKING AREAS – (Spaced caps)

(Please rule as shown)

(Please emphasise the sentence "Staff will be denied ......")

~~A coloured sticker is to be issued to staff~~ Staff will be issued with coloured stickers ~~which must be placed in a suitable position on the windscreen~~ which must be displayed on the car windscreen. Staff will be denied entry if the sticker is not clearly visible.

(Each box to measure 38 mm (1½") wide by 25mm (1") deep)

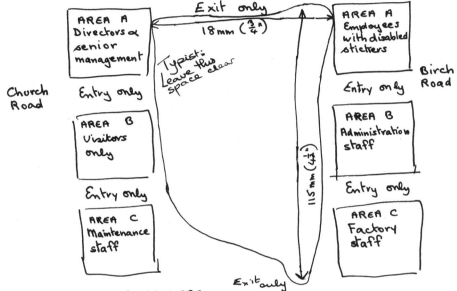

Exit only
18 mm (¾")

AREA A
Directors &
senior
management

Typist:
Leave this
space clear

AREA A
Employees
with disabled
stickers

Church
Road

Birch
Road

Entry only

Entry only

AREA B
Visitors
only

AREA B
Administration
staff

Entry only

115 mm (4½")

Entry only

AREA C
Maintenance
staff

AREA C
Factory
staff

Exit only

COLOURS OF STICKERS

Area A left – blue
Area B left – yellow
Area C left – brown

(leave 50 mm (2") across by 25 mm (1") here)

Area A right – red
Area B right – green
Area C right – orange

(✓) Area C only will be manned ~~between~~ after the hours of 6 pm and 7 am. Staff working late are asked to make special arrangements with security staff for a night pass to be issued. ~~This will give entry to~~

Forms and straight — line diagrams

Dear

<u>Emphasise third</u> paragraph. Change 'meeting' to 'conference' here and in accompanying task.

Due to the recent expansion of the company's business, ~~and the recruitment of nearly 20 new managers,~~ it has been decided to hold a meeting of bookshop managers. This should be taking place within the next four months and ~~p~~ is likely to become an annual event.

, if it proves successful,

It is envisaged that the meeting will be scheduled over two full days. The venue ✓will be ~~an hotel~~ in the East Midlands.

Please complete the tear-off slip below ~~at your earliest convenience~~ and return it to our head office by the end of the week. Further details will be sent ~~out immediately~~ to you as soon as the dates and a suitable venue have been confirmed.

Yours sincerely

Eric Winterton
Director
PRAXI BOOKSHOPS LTD

typist: please make a tear-off slip with the following details for completion, leaving <u>two</u> lines for agenda items:

NAME – BOOKSHOP ADDRESS – HOME ADDRESS – BUSINESS & HOME TELEPHONE NUMBERS – SUGGESTION(S) FOR AGENDA – DATES NOT AVAILABLE (DUE TO HOLIDAYS ETC) OVER NEXT FOUR MONTHS – DATE OF JOINING COMPANY

13 + 7 = 20

line 3½ inch from bottom of paper

35

SPACED →

PRAXI

PRAXI BOOKSHOPS LTD ← (spaced capitals)

SUGGESTED BOOKSHOP LAYOUT

TUS   (leave 4 linespaces
        clear here)   through recent discussions

It has been found that the following floor layout
has resulted in higher sales. Bearing in mind
that not all floor areas are identical in shape,
                to adhere as closely as possible
please try ~~your best to stick~~ to this layout.
~~Any comments would be welcomed.~~

REAR OF PREMISES

STATIONERY   GREETINGS CARDS

PLEASE ARRANGE   ↑ 50mm
OTHER CATEGORIES   ←75mm→ 40   (2")
AS YOU SEE FIT.   (3")   please
                             leave
                             at least
                             this space
TILL   BARGAIN   TILL
            BOOKS

FRONT OF PREMISES
(ENTRANCE AND EXIT)

TU9   ↑38mm   (leave clear) - please
        (1½")   type next paragraph
           75mm (3")   to the right of this space
        ← 36 →

In shops where there are both front and rear
✓ doors, ~~at least~~ one till, together with a
bargain ~~books~~ table, should be positioned near
           Stationery and 'greetings cards'
each. ~~Smaller items, including cards, pens, etc,~~
should be placed as far away as possible from
the doors.

Any comments on the above layout will be
discussed at the forthcoming bookshop
managers' meeting.

24
36

minutes

Task 4.3 – form

PRAXI SERIES II

_INTRODUCTION

Typist: change Praxi Series II to Praxi Series III in this task and the next.

The aim of this book is to assist you to use and understand your Praxi Series II fitted oven and grill unit.

Please read the instructions ~~given in the book~~ with care & always keep the booklet handy for ~~future~~ reference, and guidance

You have ~~bought a good~~ purchased a quality cooker and when looked after it will provide you with many ~~years of~~ ~~years of~~ good service. If, however, you ~~should be unlucky~~ ~~be unfortunate~~ and have problems, please contact your supplier in the first instance ~~who will check the appliance~~ ~~before contacting us~~.

To assist the disabled user in handling the appliance, adaptors are available to allow you to fit a specially designed tap handle. For the blind user, oven control knobs marked in braille are available. Please contact your supplier if you need any of these special aids.

All packaging materials and protective film must be removed before operating the appliance; please refer to installation and servicing notes.

Please complete the tear off slip below for membership of our user's club.

Typist: ~~Draft a reply slip~~ leave spaces for following details

Surname   ~~Forename(s)~~   Address   Telephone number
~~Separate lines~~
Name and address of supplier   Date appliance fitted

Serial number

A stamped, addressed envelope must be included with the reply slip.

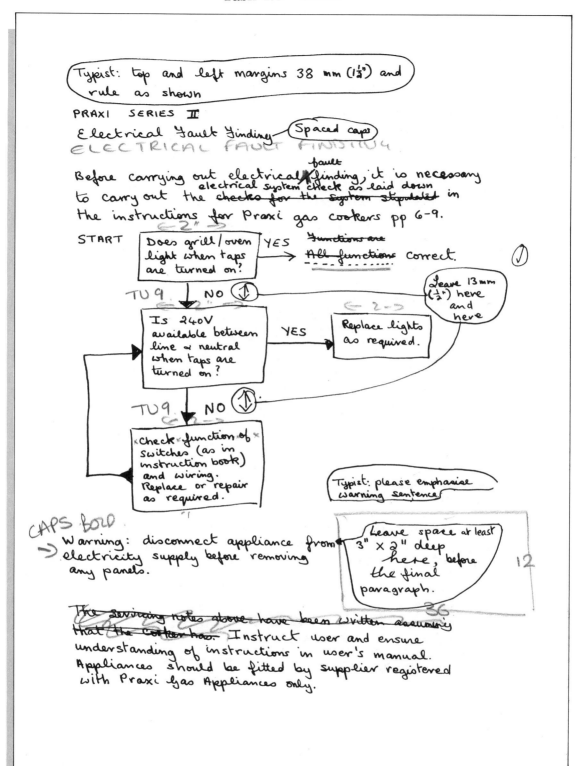

Typist: top and left margins 38 mm (1½") and rule as shown

PRAXI SERIES II

Electrical Fault Finding — Spaced caps

ELECTRICAL FAULT FINDING

Before carrying out electrical fault finding, it is necessary to carry out the electrical system check as laid down in the instructions for Praxi gas cookers pp 6-9.

START — Does grill/oven light when taps are turned on? — YES → All functions correct. ✓

TU9. NO ⇕

Is 240V available between line & neutral when taps are turned on? — YES → Replace lights as required.

Leave 13mm (½") here and here

TU9. NO ⇕

Check function of switches (as in instruction book) and wiring. Replace or repair as required.

Typist: please emphasise warning sentence

CAPS BOLD

Warning: disconnect appliance from electricity supply before removing any panels.

Leave space at least 3" × 2" deep here, before the final paragraph.

The servicing notes above have been written assuming that the cooker has. Instruct user and ensure understanding of instructions in user's manual. Appliances should be fitted by supplier registered with Praxi Gas Appliances only.

please type, giving prominence to the final paragraph of the letter.   Please also change 'North' to 'Central' here and in the accompanying chart

Dear Retailer

read in the press

As you may have ~~heard~~, we are in the process of redesigning our complete range of domestic tile products. This includes ceramic wall tiles for kitchens and bathrooms, as well as self-adhesive floor tiles.

writing to invite you to

I am now ~~taking this opportunity to write to you about~~ an exhibition of the new designs, to be held within the next few weeks at our ~~North~~ *Central* London showrooms. The exhibition will take place ~~from 6pm~~ on a weekday evening. Refreshments will be provided. *and the date should be confirmed shortly*

All you need to do is complete the tear-off slip below ~~with all the relevant details~~ and return it to me as soon as possible.

I am sure you will be delighted with our new designs.

Yours faithfully

Rachel Allen
Marketing Director

please make a tear-off slip here, with the following headings for completion, giving at least two lines for addresses:

NAME, BUSINESS ADDRESS, HOME ADDRESS, BUSINESS AND HOME TELEPHONE NUMBERS, AVAILABILITY, DATE, SIGNATURE

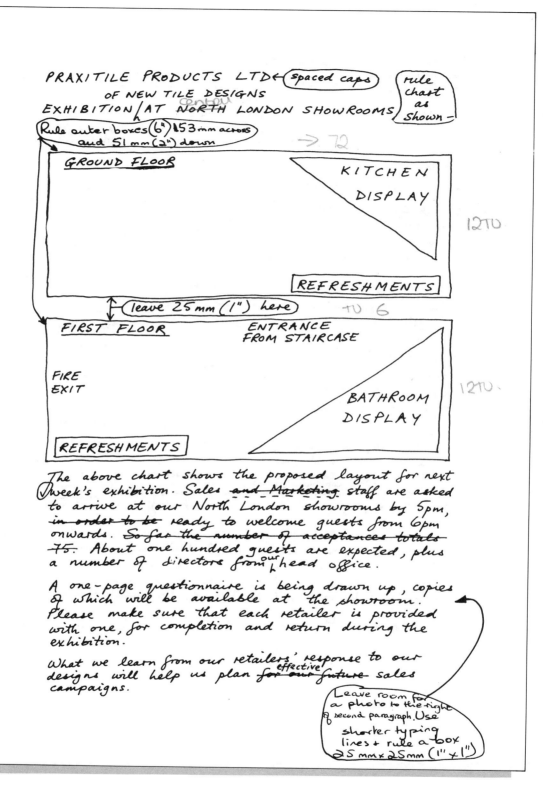

PRAXITILE PRODUCTS LTD [spaced caps] [rule chart as shown –]
OF NEW TILE DESIGNS
EXHIBITION/AT NORTH LONDON SHOWROOMS

[Rule outer boxes (6") 153 mm across and 51 mm (2") down] → 72

GROUND FLOOR

KITCHEN DISPLAY

REFRESHMENTS

12TU

[leave 25 mm (1") here]   TU 6

FIRST FLOOR   ENTRANCE FROM STAIRCASE

FIRE EXIT

BATHROOM DISPLAY

REFRESHMENTS

12TU

The above chart shows the proposed layout for next week's exhibition. Sales ~~and Marketing~~ staff are asked to arrive at our North London showrooms by 5pm, ~~in order to be~~ ready to welcome guests from 6pm onwards. ~~So far the number of acceptances totals 75.~~ About one hundred guests are expected, plus a number of directors from ^our^ head office.

A one-page questionnaire is being drawn up, copies of which will be available at the showroom. Please make sure that each retailer is provided with one, for completion and return during the exhibition.

What we learn from our retailers' response to our designs will help us plan ~~for our future~~ ^effective^ sales campaigns.

[Leave room for a photo to the right of second paragraph. Use shorter typing lines + rule a box 25 mm × 25 mm (1" × 1")]

Please leave sufficient space for letter to be reproduced on headed paper; also at points marked ⊗ and as instructed below.

Today's date

⊗

Typist: change Praxi Medical Block to Praxi Medical Centre throughout this letter & the plan which follows

Dear ⊗

PRAXI MEDICAL BLOCK

✓ Everybody concerned with the Praxiteles Group will be ~~pleased to~~ delighted to ~~know~~ that the new centre is nearly complete and will be opened on (Typist: leave enough space for day, date, month + year.) at ⊗ (Room needed for the time to be inserted later)

The opening ceremony will be performed by Typist: we are waiting confirmation from Sir John Massey – leave enough space and will be ~~followed~~ by a lunch held in the Group's John Adam Suite. An invitation is extended to you and ⊗ guests to attend this ~~occasion~~ special occasion. You are asked to reply no later than ⊗ by writing to the above address or by ringing the organiser (Tel: ⊗).

The Praxi Medical Block will fulfil a need expressed by the Group for many years. Clearly a company with ~~so many employees on its payroll~~ such a large workforce should not have to rely on first aid provision only. The opening ~~of the factory which operates for 24 hours~~ of the continuous process factory has meant that the employment of trained medical staff is an absolute necessity.

The centre will contain everything for the treatment of all save major accidents. A doctor will attend for 4 hours each day and will be "on call" after that time. X-ray staff and physiotherapy staff will be on hand to provide treatment services.

I do hope that you will be able to join us.

Yours sincerely

A Friar
Director

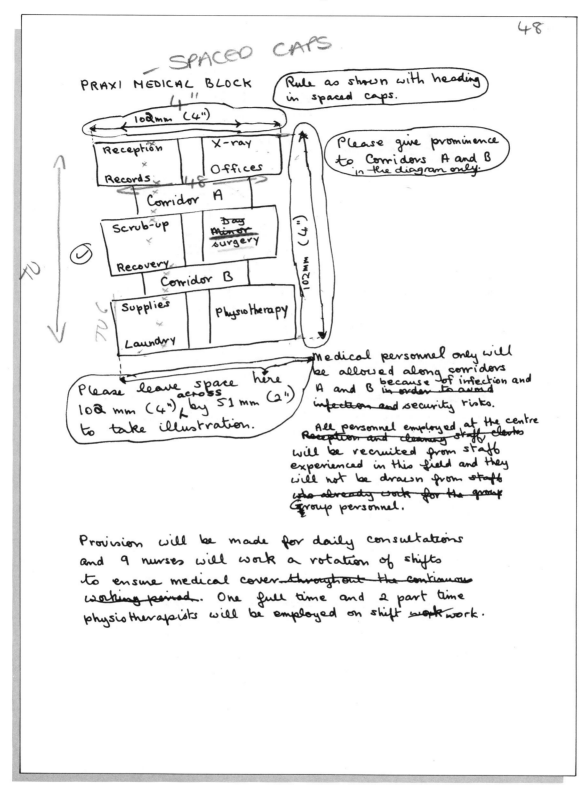

48

— SPACED CAPS

PRAXI MEDICAL BLOCK

Rule as shown with heading in spaced caps.

Please give prominence to Corridors A and B in the diagram only.

102mm (4")

| Reception | X-ray |
| Records | Offices |

Corridor A

| Scrub-up | ~~Day~~ ~~Minor~~ surgery |
| Recovery | |

Corridor B

| Supplies | Physiotherapy |
| Laundry | |

102mm (4")

24   40

Please leave space here 102 mm (4") across by 51 mm (2") to take illustration.

Medical personnel only will be allowed along corridors A and B because of infection and ~~in order to avoid infection and~~ security risks.

All personnel employed at the centre ~~Reception and cleaning staff clerks~~ will be recruited from staff experienced in this field and they will not be drawn from ~~staff who already work for the group~~ Group personnel.

Provision will be made for daily consultations and 9 nurses will work a rotation of shifts to ensure medical cover ~~throughout the continuous working period~~. One full time and 2 part time physiotherapists will be employed on shift ~~work~~ work.

Dear

> please give prominence to the third paragraph — change 'Purcell' to 'Wigmore' here and in accompanying task

We recently sent you details of a series of concerts). I am now writing to offer you up to three ^complimentary tickets for next week's ~~concert~~, to be held at the Purcell Hall.

(above "recently": that ~~we are~~ promoting)
(below "three": guitar recital)

Each of these tickets will entitle the holder to a top-price seat in the stalls, ~~as well as attendance~~ and we shall be delighted to welcome yourself and your guests to a small ✓reception, ~~to be~~ held in the Green Room after the concert.

Please complete the tear-off slip below, stating the number of tickets you require. Please also ~~give us some idea as to~~ whether you and any of your guests will be attending the reception, so that we may plan for catering.

(above "give us some idea": let us know)

Yours sincerely

Emma Strauss
Director
PRAXI CONCERT AGENCY

> typist: please make a tear-off slip here, with the following details for completion:
>
> NAME, ADDRESS, DAYTIME & EVENING TELEPHONE NUMBERS, NUMBER OF TICKETS REQUIRED, NUMBER ATTENDING RECEPTION, DATE, SIGNATURE

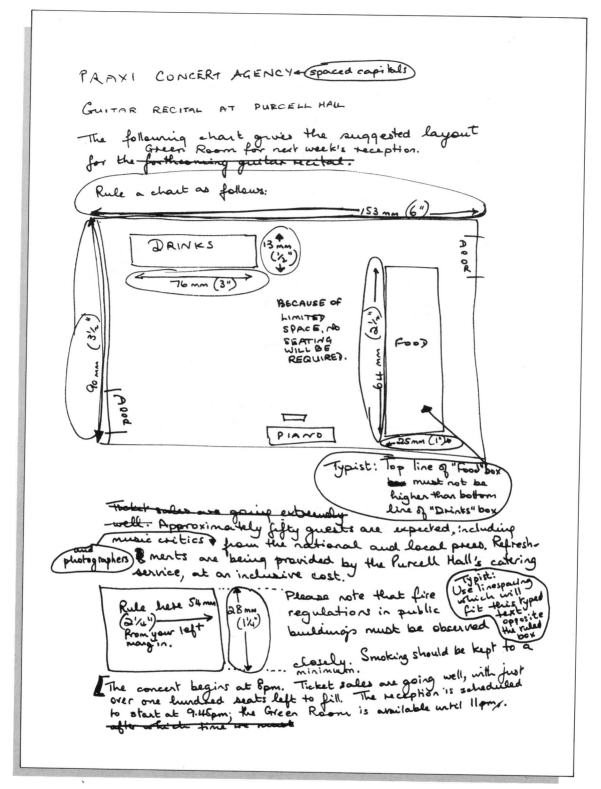

PRAXI CONCERT AGENCY (spaced capitals)

GUITAR RECITAL AT PURCELL HALL

The following chart gives the suggested layout
for the ~~forthcoming guitar recital.~~ Green Room for next week's reception.

Rule a chart as follows:

153 mm (6")

DRINKS

13 mm (½")

76 mm (3")

DOOR

90 mm (3½") DOOR

BECAUSE OF
LIMITED
SPACE, NO
SEATING
WILL BE
REQUIRED.

64 mm (2½")

FOOD

PIANO

25 mm (1")

Typist: Top line of "Food" box ~~box~~ must not be higher than bottom line of "Drinks" box

~~Ticket sales are going extremely well.~~ Approximately fifty guests are expected, including music critics (and photographers) from the national and local press. Refreshments are being provided by the Purcell Hall's catering service, at an inclusive cost.

Rule here 54mm (2¼") from your left margin.

28 mm (1⅛")

Please note that fire regulations in public buildings must be observed closely. Smoking should be kept to a minimum.

Typist: Use linespacing which will fit this typed text opposite the ruled box

[The concert begins at 8pm. Ticket sales are going well, with just over one hundred seats left to fill. The reception is scheduled to start at 9.45pm; the Green Room is available until 11pm. ~~after which time we must~~

PRAXI FASHION SHOW

Typist: please change Praxi Fashion Show to Praxi Fashion Parade every time when you type this draft for a publicity leaflet.

Have you got your tickets yet for the fashion parade of the decade? As a holder of a Praxi Gold Card and a regular subscriber to our fashionable magazine you are entitled to a ✓ ticket for yourself and one for ~~a friend~~ yr partner.

Emphasise name of hotel

The parade will be held on Easter Saturday in the ballroom of the Park Royal Hotel in London. If you send back the reply slip below, your name will go into ✓ a prize draw. The winners ~~will attend~~ will see the Parisian showing of the parade and will be our special guests at the glittering Louis XIV restaurant ~~where the stars gather when they are in Paris~~. In addition to the fabulous parade you will see the sights on an accompanied tour of Paris. You can shop for souvenirs in the fashionable markets and buy luxurious clothes and accessories in the shops. At night you will take a boat trip down the river and see sparkling Paris by night.

PRAXI FASHION SHOW

Typist: please draft a reply slip with spaces for the following information.

NAME   ADDRESS   HOME & BUSINESS TEL NOS
CARD NO   SUBSCRIPTION NO
NAME OF FRIEND   ADDRESS

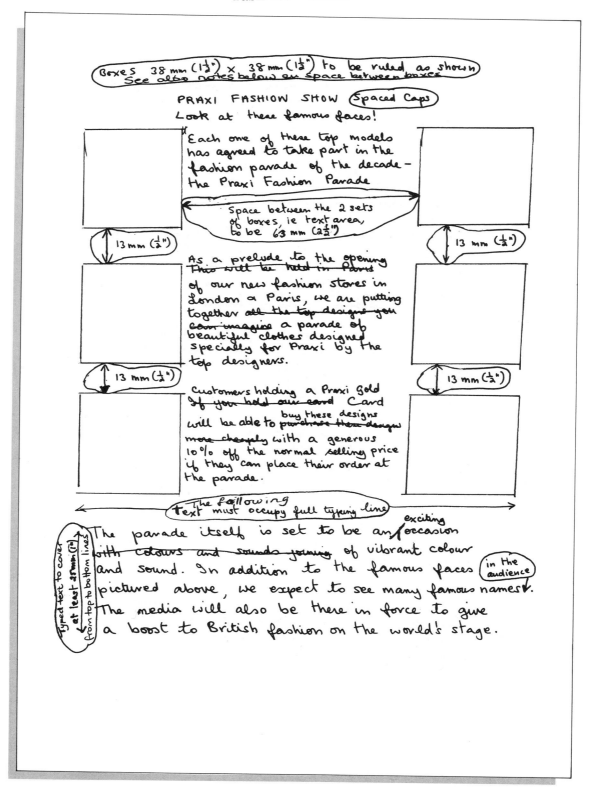

Boxes 38 mm (1½") x 38 mm (1½") to be ruled as shown
See also notes below on space between boxes

PRAXI FASHION SHOW (Spaced Caps)
Look at these famous faces!

"Each one of these top models has agreed to take part in the fashion parade of the decade – the Praxi Fashion Parade

Space between the 2 sets of boxes, ie text area, to be 63 mm (2½")

13 mm (½")   13 mm (½")

As a prelude to the opening
This will be held in Paris
of our new fashion stores in London & Paris, we are putting together all the top designs you can imagine a parade of beautiful clothes designed specially for Praxi by the top designers.

13 mm (½")   13 mm (½")

Customers holding a Praxi Gold
If you hold our card Card
                        buy these designs
will be able to purchase these design
more cheaply with a generous 10% off the normal selling price if they can place their order at the parade.

The following
Text must occupy full typing line

Typed text to cover at least 25mm (1") from top to bottom lines

The parade itself is set to be an exciting occasion
with colours and sounds joining of vibrant colour and sound. In addition to the famous faces (in the audience) pictured above, we expect to see many famous names. The media will also be there in force to give a boost to British fashion on the world's stage.

Task 4.8 – form

Dear Customer

Thank you for your recent letter. ~~regarding the unsatisfactory state of one of our products.~~ I was sorry to hear that the product you purchased was not entirely to your satisfaction.

[margin note, boxed: Give prominence to fourth paragraph, & change 'strawberry' to 'fruit' here and in accompanying task]

Perhaps I should explain that confusion over jar labelling was the cause of the problem. We are now in the process of redesigning ✓ ~~some of~~ our labels, and hope that this will ~~put an end to the problem.~~ t remedy the situation.

We are sending to you today under separate cover a full refund, ~~of the purchase price~~ together with a replacement jar of strawberry preserve. *(, which we hope will be to your liking)*

For our records, I wonder if you would be kind enough to complete the tear-off slip below, and return it to us in the pre-paid envelope provided. ← *[note, circled: Typist: Use full stop, not question mark]*

Yours faithfully

Samantha Floyd
Public Relations Officer
PRAXI JAMS & PRESERVES LTD

Enc

[boxed note: typist: please make a tear-off slip here, with the following details for completion: NAME, ADDRESS, TELEPHONE NUMBER, PLACE OF PURCHASE & PURCHASE PRICE, DESCRIPTION OF PRODUCT, DATE, SIGNATURE]

PRAXI JAMS & PRESERVES LTD

NEW LABEL DESIGNS (spaced capitals)

Just lately we have been receiving complaints regarding the contents of our special strawberry preserves. This problem ~~has apparently been~~ seems to have ~~caused~~ arisen because labels for jams and for preserves are similar in appearance, and have been getting confused.

The diagrams below show the updated designs. These labels are being printed at the moment, and should be ~~despatched to us very shortly.~~ ready for use within the next two weeks.

(Each "label" to be ruled 64mm x 64mm (2½" x 2½"))

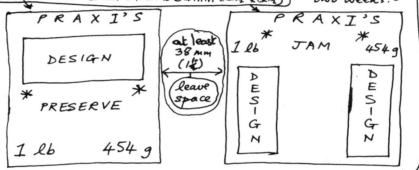

P R A X I 'S

DESIGN

*   PRESERVE   *

1 lb   454 g

at least 38mm (1½") leave space

P R A X I 'S

1 lb * JAM * 454g

D E S I G N

D E S I G N

(Name of fruit will be indicated between asterisks.)

leave at least 64mm (2½") clear

In the meantime, it is most important that labels are not confused. Please check all stock, to ensure that there are no strawberry preserve labels ~~mixed in~~ with those for jams. ✓ ~~Thank you for your co-operation.~~

for different products

(Typist: Please type this text over space of 51 mm (2"))

5 Tables

Task 5.1

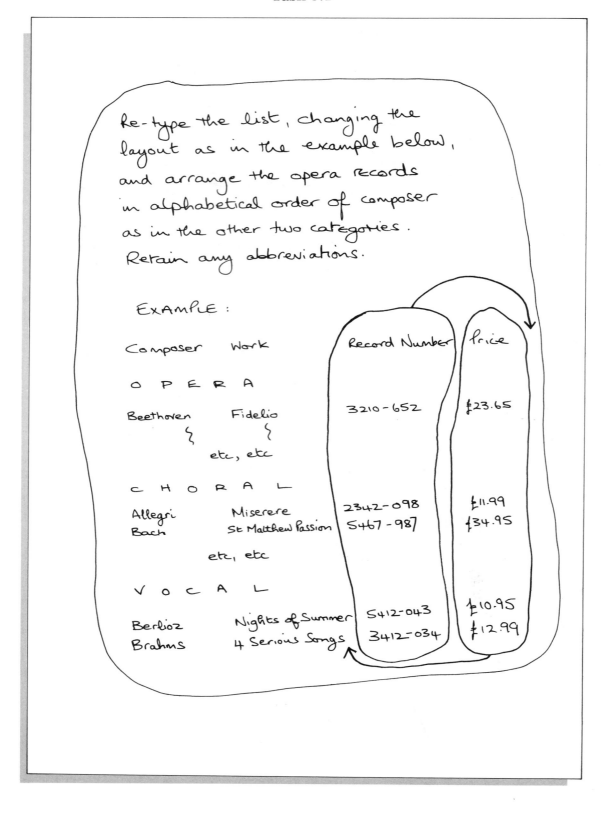

Re-type the list, changing the layout as in the example below, and arrange the opera records in alphabetical order of composer as in the other two categories. Retain any abbreviations.

EXAMPLE:

Composer	Work	Record Number	Price
O P E R A			
Beethoven	Fidelio	3210-652	£23.65
{	{		
	etc, etc		
C H O R A L			
Allegri	Miserere	2342-098	£11.99
Bach	St Matthew Passion	5467-987	£34.95
	etc, etc		
V O C A L			
Berlioz	Nights of Summer	5412-043	£10.95
Brahms	4 Serious Songs	3412-034	£12.99

Centre Both.

CLASSICAL RECORDINGSX-XBASIC STOCK ← (centre)
X
X
— dont underline this.
Opera, Choral and Vocal* ← (centre)
X
X

O P E R A

3) Bizet: Carmen   2347-567 £21.97
10) Verdi: Traviata   4567-213 £32.97
2) Bellini: Puritani   7436-543 £32.97
5) Mozart: Marriage of Figaro 5489-216 £33.98
6) Puccini: Boheme   7621-890 £20.98
1) Beethoven: Fidelio 3210-652 £23.65
4) Lehar: Merry Widow 3912-094 £15.90
7) Rossini: Barber of Seville 7120-345 £22.97
8) Strauss: Rosenkavalier 1235-123 £34.95
9) Tchaikovsky: Queen of Spades 8341-989 £41.99

C H O R A L

Allegri: Miserere   2342-098 £11.99
Bach: St Matthew Passion 5467-987 £34.95
Beethoven: Missa Solemnis 2312-902 £15.99
Elgar: Dream of Gerontius 2387-097 £21.00
Handel: Messiah 9821-902 £22.98
Mozart: Requiem 1279-769 £10.99
Verdi: Requiem 1234-987 £21.50

Same

V O C A L

1) Berlioz: Nights of Summer 5412-043 £10.97
2) Brahms: 4 Serious Songs 3412-034 £12.99
3) Elgar: Songs 4512-934 £13.99
4) Haydn: Songs 4519-675 £10.50
5) Mozart: Songs 2342-012 £22.97
7) Schubert: Songs 9821-098 £12.99
8) Schumann: Liederkreis 3256-043 £11.50
6) Ravel: Chansons 3462-236 £23.97
9) Verdi: Songs 6542-023 £10.97

*The above records are to be kept in stock at all times. Should any of them be "out of stock" at the suppliers, consult the Manager of the Music Department. She will advise on other records to stock as a temporary measure. A separate list of records of orchestral, instrumental and chamber music has been compiled. This should be consulted if enquiries for those types of music are received. If in doubt, consult Jean Bastedo, Records Buyer, extension 95.

Task 5.2

Please extract the details from the table opposite for those employees of the South Western Transport Department of Praxiteles Group from the Construction, Quarries and Special Products Divisions who have a car leased to them. Please re-arrange the names into alphabetical order under these three divisions as shown in the example (✳) below. Retain any abbreviations.

CAR LEASING FROM NEW LOMBARD CAR LEASING COMPANY

PRAXITELES GROUP ← (spaced capitals)
(South Western Transport Department)   (centre these 2 lines)

The following is an up-to-date schedule of the company's commitment for this year. The proposed new contracts will involve cars for all staff at scale 2 and above.

(✳)

NAME	POSITION	MAKE/MODEL OF VEHICLE	REGISTRATION NO
Construction Division			
G Blackman	General Manager	Ford Granada 2.8 Ghia	E369 ECH
S Brown	Chief Engineer	Ford Sierra 2.0 Ghia	E246 FVP
D Clarke	Works Manager	Ford Sierra 2.0 LX	E247 FVP
Quarries Division			
D Evans	Geologist	Ford Sierra 2.0 LX	E490 FVO
Special Products Division			
L George	Accounts Director	Ford Sierra 2.0 LX	F449 EMO

*Awaiting delivery ← (centre)

NB Most cars are now fitted with a radio and cassette. An electronic anti-theft security device is encoded at the time of delivery. Every window is etched with the car's registration number. There is also a security alarm to protect the vehicle. Please ensure that your personnel are made aware of these security measures.

Task 5.2 — continued

```
NEW LOMBARD CAR LEASING COMPANY

MAKE        MODEL            REG NO      LEASED TO

Ford        Granada 2.8 Ghia  E367 ECH   P Hitchins    Finance Director     (CS)  / — ②

            Granada 2.8 Ghia  E369 ECH   G Blackman    General Manager      (C) — ①

            Sierra 2.0 Ghia   E246 FVP   S Brown       Chief Engineer       (C) — ②

            Sierra 2.0 LX     E247 FVP   D Clarke      Works Manager        (C) — ③

            Sierra 2.0 LX     E490 FVO   D Evans       Geologist            (Q) X — ①

            Sierra 2.0 LX     F449 EMO   X L George    Accounts Director    (SP) — ①

            Sierra 2.0 LX     E489 FVO   G White       Personnel Director   (CS) / — ④

            Sierra 2.0 LX     E491 FVO   P Smith       Works Manager        (Q) X — ⑧

            Sierra 1.6 L      E248 FVP   J Yelland     Assistant Engineer   (C) — ⑥

Vauxhall    Carlton 1.8 LI*   F524 EMM   X R Williams  Commercial Manager   (SP) — ⑤

            Cavalier 1.8 LI   F123 FMB   H Walsh       Site Engineer        (C) — ⑤

            Cavalier 1.8 LI   F124 FMB   P Burton      Recruitment Officer  (CS) / — ①

            Cavalier 1.6 L    F422 CVB   X G Westway   Research Manager     (SP) — ④

            Cavalier 1.6 L    F423 CVB   E Perks       Safety Officer       (Q) X — ②

Opel        Manta             F221 HRC   F Toms        Technical Manager    (Q) X — ④

Austin      Montego 1.6 L     E696 ORA   X D Thomas    Works Manager        (SP) — ③

            Montego 1.6 L     E697 ORA   C Wainwright  Recruitment          (CS) / — ③

            Montego 1.6 L     E698 ORA   F Moore       Contracts Manager    (C) — ④

            Maestro 1.6 L     F669 GMB   X W Johns     Sales Manager        (SP) — ②
```

<u>Key</u>   (C) = Construction Division 6   (Q) = Quarries Division 4
       (CS) = Central Services Division 4   (SP) = Special Products Division 5

* Awaiting delivery   —> Centre.

49

Task 5.3

Re-type the table, changing the
layout to 2 columns, as in the
example below, indenting the titles 4
as shown
or 3 spaces. Arrange the book titles
by Malcolm Arne in alphabetical
order, like those of the other
authors

Example:

FICTION   NON-FICTION

Malcolm Arne   Jodie Bawdhury
    Battle Commences   The Art of Indian Cooking
4   etc   3   Indonesian Cuisine *
spaces   spaces   etc
here   here

                                 Henry Bagley
                                     Better Tennis Strokes
                                         etc
Gwen Bailey
    A Dissolute Woman
Aelen Morgan - A Life   Mary Henley
    etc   Dried Flower Arrangements
                                         etc.

        etc , etc ...

50

Task 5.3 – continued

PRAXI BOOKS ← ⟨spaced caps + centre⟩   *SPACED CAPS + CENTRE

Here is a selection of our best selling fiction and⟩ ⟨centre⟩ ← CENTRE
non-fiction titles

FICTION   NON-FICTION

Malcolm Arne

3 ⑤ Death Before Dishonour, ④ Cyanide Is A Solution, ① Battle Commences,
3 ③ Camel Command, ⑦ Ten Little Terrorists, ⑨ Return To New York,   ⟩ 10
   ⑧ Revenge Is Sweet, Vengeance Extracted, ⑥ More Than Reason Allows,
   ② Be My Betrayer

Gwen Bailey
3 A Dissolute Woman, Helen Morgan – A Life, My Cup Runs Over

Betty Brown
3 More Tales Of Tremaine, The Saga Of Tremaine, The Tremaine
   Inheritance

Mary Richards
3 A Better Man Than I, The More I See You

Peter Richmond
3 Blake's Fall, Never Talk To A Stranger, Paper Tiger

NON-FICTION

Jodie Baudhury
The Art Of Indian Cooking, Indonesian Cuisine*, Middle Eastern
Cookery

Henry Bagley
Better Tennis Strokes*, Squash Tips For All*

Mary Henley
Dried Flower Arrangements, Flower Arranging Made Easy,
The Furniture Of The Garden, The Small Gardener*

Frank Innes
Fitness For The Family, Get Fit With Frank*, Workouts For Men And Women*

Vashti and Kamlesh Sumra
The Fish Dishes Of Goa, Oriental Cookery

Henry Thomas
Classical Music Today

Paul Vega
The Popular Music Industry, Tin Pan Alley

Our latest book catalogue is now in print. You may
collect this free of charge from all our branches.

Thinking of a gift for a friend? Our friendly staff will be
happy to gift wrap any purchase free of charge.

* Available in hardback and paperback

Task 5.4

Type a table of information extracted from the list opposite, as shown below at ☒

Centre these 2 lines

A D U L T   C O N T I N U I N G   E D U C A T I O N

Distict Principal: A Hicks MA   Assistant Principal: B Reid BSc

COLLEGE OF FURTHER EDUCATION (BUSINESS STUDIES) CARETAKER — T HILLMAN

Spring Term Courses (Centre)

CENTRE

CENTRE

Classes commence the second week of January. If you have difficulty finding your room, please enquire at the caretaker's office. This is situated on the left of the main entrance.

☒ List only those courses at Venue: BS - CFE. Arrange these for each day together, Mon - Thurs. Within the list for each day, arrange in ascending order of Room No. The courses for Monday have been arranged for you in the example below, showing headings required:

Room No	Course Name	Time	Headings in Capitals
6	Italian for your Holidays (Monday)	7-9 pm	
8	French for your Holidays	7-9 pm	
12	Computing - An Introduction	7-9 pm	
14	Information Technology	6-8 pm	
Tuesday			
1	Word Processing RSA I	10-12 noon	
⎨	⎨	⎨	

It would be appreciated if evening class lecturers would switch off all equipment and lights and close all windows and doors before leaving the classroom. The college doors will be locked at 9.30 pm every evening unless special arrangements are made prior to the evening class. In case of an emergency, please ring St Austell 875208.

* subject to room change - check notice board each week.

ADULT CONTINUING EDUCATION - SPRING TERM COURSES

Classes commence the second week of January

COURSE NAME	TIME	DAY	DURATION IN WEEKS	VENUE	ROOM NO
Italian for your Holidays	7-9 pm	Mon	5	BS - CFE	6
French for your Holidays	7-9 pm	Mon	10	BS - CFE	8
Computing - An Introduction	7-9 pm	Mon	20	BS - CFE	12
Information Technology	6-8 pm	Mon	10	BS - CFE	14
Art - Drawing for Beginners	7-9 pm	Thurs	10	SFC	B8
Art - Paint the Sea	10-12 noon	Tues	10	SFC	B8
Dance - Tap Dancing	7-9 pm	Mon	5	SFC	A1
Dance to Pop Music	7-9 pm	Thurs	5	SFC	A1
Furniture Restoration	7-9 pm	Tues	10	SFC	C5
Needlework for Pleasure	6-8 pm	Tues	10	SFC	C3
Typewriting - Advanced	5.30-7 pm	Wed	20	BS - CFE	22
Typewriting for Beginners	5.30-7 pm	Tues	20	BS - CFE	22
Typewriting Retake RSA II	7-9 pm	Thurs	20	BS - CFE	22
Word Processing RSA I	10-12 noon	Tues	10	BS - CFE	1
Word Processing RSA II	7-9 pm	Thurs	10	BS - CFE	1
Word Processing RSA III	7-9 pm	Wed	10	BS - CFE	1
Boat Building and Repairing	7-9 pm	Mon	10	S - CFE	302
China Painting	7-9 pm	Mon	10	S - CFE	206
Ladies Keep Fit	10-12 noon	Wed	10	S - CFE	216
Photography	10-12 noon	Wed	5	SFC	A4
Photography for Beginners	7-9 pm	Wed	5	SFC	A4
Yoga for Health*	6-8 pm	Thurs	10	BS - CFE	32
Yoga - Over 50s*	10-12 noon	Wed	10	BS - CFE	32
Woodwork	6-8 pm	Thurs	10	S - CFE	302
Bridge - Improvers Course	2-4 pm	Wed	5	SFC	B6
Car Maintenance	7-9 pm	Wed	10	S - CFE	304
Machine Knitting	9-11 am	Mon	10	S - CFE	212
Self Defence	10-12 noon	Tues	5	S - CFE	216
Tennis for Beginners	2-4 pm	Sat	5	S - CFE	Hall
Stockmarket - Continuation*	6.30-8 pm	Wed	10	BS - CFE	5
Spanish for your Holidays	7-9 pm	Wed	10	BS - CFE	8
Music - Enjoying Singing	7-9 pm	Thurs	5	SFC	A2
Greek Made Simple	6.30-8 pm	Tues	10	BS - CFE	8
Pottery	7-9 pm	Wed	10	SFC	A6

* subject to room change - check notice board each week.

Task 5.5

Compile and type a table showing the following information, taking the details from the schedule opposite:

Heading: see below *

Share	Investor's Name	Holding	Market Value £
Barclays Bank	D Ball	250	1,030
}	}	}	}
BAT Industries	D Ball	180	811
}	etc		

List the shares in alphabetical order. List Investors' Names in alphabetical order for each share.

Type Investors' Names with initial capitals only.

Retain any abbreviations.

* Heading: PRAXITELES GROUP
Investors' Holdings (centre both lines)

General Note (centre) — CENTRE *

Under the current rules a PEP investor must be over 18 and resident in the UK for tax purposes. Only one PEP can be taken out in each calendar year. The maximum investment is currently £3,000. Provided that no withdrawals are made from the PEP until the start of the third year, all income is free from UK taxation. After that time, the PEP can be retained as a tax-free shelter, but withdrawals can be made without penalty.

Personal Equity Plans need to be regarded as long-term investments. They will then accumulate substantial funds which are free from income tax.

Task 5.5 — continued

Investors' Holdings in Shares

① D BALL

Share	Holding	Value
Barclays Bank	250	£1,030
BAT Industries	180	£811
Hanson Trust	600	£846
		£2,687

② C CHATSFIELD

Share	Holding	Value
Barclays Bank	280	£1,153
British Gas	300	£477
Hanson Trust	900	£1,269
		£2,899

③ W CORNS

Share	Holding	Value
English China Clays	320	£1,488
Land Securities	100	£548
Legal & General	300	£879
		£2,915

④ J DAVIS

Share	Holding	Value
British Gas	475	£756
British Telecom	435	£1,146
TSB Group	880	£959
		£2,861

⑤ J FOX

Share	Holding	Value
Barclays Bank	250	£1,030
English China Clays	140	£651
Land Securities	230	£1,260
		£2,941

⑥ S GROSE

Share	Holding	Value
British Telecom	650	£1,709
Rolls-Royce	390	£542
		£2,251

⑦ L THOMAS

Share	Holding	Value
British Gas	800	£1,272
Hanson Trust	600	£846
		£2,118

⑧ F WATSON

Share	Holding	Value
BAT Industries	300	£1,353
Land Securities	200	£1,096
Rolls-Royce	300	£417
		£2,866

Barclays Bank
BAT Industries
British Gas
British Telecom — English China Clays
Hanson Trust
Land Securities
Legal & General
Rolls-Royce
TSB Group

Put the videos in alphabetical order — "Bird", "The Bedroom Window", "La Boheme", "Buster", etc and change the layout to a table with headings in the following form:

Title	Description	Format	Rental per night £
"Bird"	The story of jazz saxophonist	VHS only	1.75

(Spaced caps)   (Retain abbreviation for VHS and Beta)

PRAXI VIDEO RENTAL

OUR TOP TEN VIDEOS   (centre both headings)

* SPACED CAPS + CENTRE BOTH

£1.75 per night:

"Bird" – The story of jazz saxophonist Charlie Parker directed by Clint Eastwood VHS only

"A Fish called Wanda" – An hilarious comedy starring John Cleese and Jamie Lee Curtis VHS/Beta *

"Buster" – Starring Phil Collins, the story of the Great Train Robber VHS only

"Who framed Roger Rabbit?" – The film comedy that combines live action and cartoon characters VHS only *

"Willow" – A fantasy featuring demons, dragons and dwarfs VHS/Beta

£1.50 per night:

"The Bedroom Window" – Thriller revolving around a false witness VHS/Beta

"Fatal Attraction" – The smash hit of 1988, a TERRIFYING love story VHS/Beta

"Sunset" – A comedy tribute to the twilight of the great Hollywood silent era VHS only

"War Requiem" – A demanding epic of mourning for the Great War VHS only

"La Boheme" – Intelligent adaptation of Puccini's opera of doomed romance VHS only

If you are not yet a member of Praxi Video Club why not think about joining?

Life membership £50.00
Annual membership £3.50   (centre both lines)

We also offer an insurance against damage to or loss of video films at the very reasonable sum of £3.00 per annum.

*These two videos are extremely popular and we recommend that you reserve them a week in advance.

Centre

⑥

6 Past exam papers

– Part 1 – Autumn 1988

EXAMINATIONS BOARD

TYPEWRITING SKILLS
STAGE III (ADVANCED) - PART 1
TUESDAY 22 NOVEMBER 1988

(TIME ALLOWED - ONE AND A QUARTER HOURS)

Notes for candidates

1. Please write or type your name and centre number on each piece of *← time at end*
    your work.

2. Please assemble your completed work in the order in which it is
    presented in this paper and cross through any work which you do *← " " "*
    not wish to be marked.

3. Calculators, English and mother-tongue dictionaries on-line
    spellcheckers and centre-prepared or manufacturers' machine manuals
    may be used in the examination.

4. This paper includes Tasks 1, 2, 3 and 4 which form the whole
    of Part 1 of the examination. One item of information to be
    incorporated into Task 3 will be announced during the course of
    this part of the examination. *postcard.*

You must:

1. Complete all four tasks. *← fail if dont finish.*

2. Use only the stationery provided in your answer book.

3. Letters and memos: insert today's date and take one carbon copy
    of each, unless otherwise instructed.

4   Correct typographical errors, obvious errors of agreement and
    spelling errors which may appear in any task but will **not** be
    indicated in the draft.

(Penalties will be incurred if these instructions are not followed.)

TSIII-1 (Autumn 1988)   ©RSA 1988

TASK 1   -2-

22nd Nov. 1988 , 1 top copy

(one routed)
type on top copy
2 carbon.

1 + 2

Our Ref DH/FW3

Mr C Evans, 43 Chapel Lane, LLANDRINDOD WELLS,
Powys LD4 3AZ

Dr Mr Evans

WELSH CRAFT FAIR 12-16 JUNE 1989

✓ I ~~am sorry~~ I was not in when you telephoned.
As my secy explained, we too regret the closing
of The Hydro. However, this was necy for a
number of reasons. [I can however recom the new
hotel aquired by the Praxotel Group — The Snowdonia,
Marine Dr, Llandudno. Altho' it does not occupy
~~the too that~~ such a commanding view as The Hydro,
we feel that it's many facilities will more than /compensate
for this.

[We hope to make this ~~hotel~~ the best in the area, both from
the point of view of a ~~confo~~ bus centre and also a holiday
venue. The enclosed ~~details~~ brochure will give you details
of the hotel's amenities and the Conference Centre.

Most of our guests are surprised to find two
swimming ~~pools~~ and 3 restaurants within one
complex, for example!

I shall be in Llandudno from Mon, 5 Dec 1988 until
the ~~following~~ Sun (Typist: please give exact date) 10
✓ and I should be ~~delighted~~ to see you to discuss the
staging of the above Fair. I only has Wed free — my
diary is def full — but we could either. TU 2
(a) have lunch between 12.30 pm and 2pm, or (← 1230 hrs. 1400 hrs)
(b) dinner between 1845 hrs and 2100 hrs; ← 6.45pm 9.PM TU 2

We can then discuss poss discounts etc. I am enclosing
a pre-paid card for your reply and I am sending
a copy of this letter to Mr J Price, the Hotel Manager,
for info.

PS Clearly if you can only come for
dinner, then I should be delighted
to arrange an overnight stay
for you.

Yours scly
David Harper
Director

x
x
PSxx
x
enc
x FILE
CC xx
file

Mr J Price, Hotel Manager
file

will accept comma.

58

TASK 2   -3-

(Memo)

From David Harper   Ref DH/FW4
      Director

                         22 Nov. 1988

To   John Prescott
      Chief Accountant

WELSH CRAFT FAIR ~~call~~

⊘ I have rec'd a telephone ~~enquiry~~ from Mr C Ev—
of Ll—W—, who is arrangeing the above Fair
from— to—. He ~~looking for~~ needs accom
since the ~~place~~ hotel he usually uses, ie The H—,
has now closed.

I am suggesting that he uses The Snowdonia
and I ~~think that I would~~ would like to offer
him a 15% discount on his a/c. ✓ your comments
please! // I am going to Llandudno on
Monday, 5 December 1988. ~~Could you~~ please
let me have the advertising budget by
1 December so that the campaign can be
planned then.

(I think that the opportunities
to be gained from this are
considerable.)

Dont need
day

59

TASK 3

Please type a postcard to The Snow~~donia~~ LL30 2HE
Hotel, Mar~~ine~~ Dr~~ive~~ Ll~~andudno~~ Gwynedd (I'll
give you the postcode later) Mark the
card For the attention of Mr J Price, Manager
and date it for today.

Confirm ~~send date~~ ~~station~~ time of arrival at Llandudno
Junction at 1110 hours on Monday,
5 December 1988. Please arrange hire car
(1650 cc engine with plenty of boot space)
to be waiting. Account to go direct to
Head Office. Suggest 1530-1630 hours for
Senior Staff Briefing. Please do not arrange
any further appt (s) for me without consulting
Pauline Drew, my Personal Assistant.

post code. LL30 2HE

TASK 4

Please retype this in the order indicated by the numbers but don't type numbers! First para in double line spacing, rest in single. Top and left margins of at least 50mm (2") on each page please to take illustrations

P R A X O T E L   G R O U P

NO 75 - THE SNOWDONIA

② Elegance and style greet you immediately you step through the doorway of No 75. Dwell for just a moment and allow your eyes to absorb the beautiful antique dresser, the superb decoration and the magnificent chandelier hanging above the hand-carved spindled staircase. The feeling of ease and real comfort is readily apparent. Each of the 8 bedrooms is distinctively and luxuriously furnished. Their grace and charm are reflected by their individual names: 'Sian', 'Megan', 'Olwen' etc. The luxury of this town house is nowhere more apparent than in your bedroom. Original cast iron beds have been fully renovated and furnished with sumptuous downy pillows and duvets then clothed in French Linen. The rich drapes, extravagant wall coverings and antique furnishings create an air of peaceful tranquility.

① Welcome to No 75 - a very special annexe to a very special hotel; considered by many to be unique. Nestling at the foot of the majestic Orme in Llandudno, this Victorian town house has been completely restored and completely refurbished to capture its original splendour. As the town's first banking house, character, charm and craftsmanship were established in its appointments. Now its new owners, The Praxotel Group, have created an extravaganza in period furnishing, guaranteed to make your stay a memorable one.

④ Whilst striving to maintain a Victorian atmosphere, each room is equipped with modern technology to make your stay thoroughly relaxing and comfortable. Your room has the following facilities:

1   its own 26" remote control colour television;

2   a video recorder and access to a large library of video films;

3   satellite viewing;

4   a direct dial telephone;

5   electronic safe and trouser press;

6   a refrigerator and tea/coffee making facilities.

Finally, independent air conditioning for each room ensures your needs are conveniently catered for.

③ Your bathroom is a splendid feature to - having a genuine marble floor, **original** 'John' fittings, hair dryer and Jacuzzi bath. Of course, the fittings are gold plated! A special TV viewing screen is built into the wall so that you can relax for as long as you wish in your bath and not miss your favourite programme. Why not order a bottle of champagne to complete the picture!

~~The parent hotel - The Snowdonia - has 3 restaurants, 2 bars, 2 swimming pools, sauna and steam room at your disposal.~~

⑤ No 75 is the perfect place - whatever the occasion or celebration - to step back in time, relax and create memories for years to come. In fact, if you are celebrating a special anniversary this year, why not contact us - we offer special rates for Silver and Golden Wedding Anniversaries.

THE SNOWDONIA

⑥ Although No 75 is very special, The Snowdonia - the parent hotel - has 3 restaurants, 2 bars, 2 swimming pools, a sauna and steam room at your disposal. ~~It too has its 'luxury' bedrooms and even its standard rooms are above average.~~

EXAMINATIONS BOARD

A384 TYPEWRITING SKILLS
STAGE III (ADVANCED) - PART 1
TUESDAY 22 NOVEMBER 1988

<u>INSTRUCTIONS TO INVIGILATOR</u>

(a) Read to the candidates the Instructions.

(b) Hand to each candidate a copy of the <u>White</u> Part 1
Examination Paper and an answer book (Code W).

(c) When the candidates are ready, start the
examination.

(d) After about 15-30 minutes, if possible when most
candidates have work in their machines, candidates must
be told to stop typing.

ANNOUNCE THAT FOR TASK 3, THE POSTCODE IS LL30 2HE.

Note: this separate sheet is for the invigilator with the missing detail from the postcard task.

THE ROYAL SOCIETY OF ARTS
EXAMINATIONS BOARD
SINGLE-SUBJECT EXAMINATIONS

S396
TYPEWRITING SKILLS
STAGE III (ADVANCED)
THURSDAY 16th JUNE 1988

PART 2 (TIME ALLOWED - ONE AND A QUARTER HOURS)

Notes for candidates

1 Please write or type your name and centre number on each piece of your work.

2 Please assemble your completed work in the order in which it is presented in this paper and cross through any work which you do not wish to be marked.

3 Calculators, English Dictionaries and manufacturers' machine manuals may be used in the examinations.

4 This paper includes Tasks 5, 6, and 7 which form the whole of Part 2 of the examination.

You must:

1 Complete all three tasks.

2 Use only the stationery provided in your answer book.

(Penalties will be incurred if these instructions are not followed)

TSIII-2(Summer 1988)   © RSA 1988

TASK 5

Please type the following standard letter. Leave sufficient space at top of page for printing on headed paper and at points marked ⓧ.

July 1988

ⓧ

Dear ⓧ

sheltered Accommodation, Walkden

~~We note that~~ Praxi are pleased to announce the acquisition of a ~~new~~ site in Walkden. Building work will start immediately and by the spring of 1990 ~~it is hoped~~ we hope to be able to ~~offer~~ sheltered accommodation to 100 people. // We note that you might (from our records) qualify for residence in the new development and our Resettlement Officers will be in your area on ~~Tuesdays~~ Wednesdays during the month of ⓧ. // Please complete the tear-off slip and return it to us If you would like a visit.

Yours sincerely

← Typist leave 1 clear line space only here

Charles Baker
Manager

—

NAME ⓧ   ADDRESS ⓧ   TEL NO ⓧ
PREFERRED TIME FOR VISIT ⓧ

Typist: please use leader dots where information is to be inserted.

IMPORTANT. PLEASE CHANGE SHELTERED ACCOMMODATION TO SPECIALLY ADAPTED ACCOMMODATION THROUGHOUT THIS LETTER AND THE PLAN WHICH FOLLOWS.

TASK 6

Plan of New Development (Centre)

↕ PRAXI HOUSING ASSOCIATION   (Sp Caps & Centre)

① Magdala Court   CAR PARKING

(leave at least 25mm (1") here)

② Old* Hall   ④ Walkden Rise

(leave at least 25mm (1") here)

③ Shared ~~Privately~~ Ownership Properties ✓

~~Car parking lot~~

C A R   P A R K I N G

Warden	Sheltered Accommodation
Garden	Sheltered Accommodation
Warden	Sheltered Accommodation

* North West Headquarters of Praxi Housing Association

Typist: Please give emphasis to the words in the numbered boxes but DO NOT type the numbers.

TASK 7

Typist: Please select the tenants from Areas A, B and C from the accompanying list and type the information under the following headings:—

NAME   AREA   AGE   HARR   LARR   SSR   (Typist: there is no need to rule)

Mrs M Bickerstaffe   B   59   X

When you have selected the names, put them in alphabetical order (not by area) and use a capital X to indicate whether they have been recommended by the Local Authority, Social Services or part of the Housing Association Register. At the foot of the table type the following paragraph:—

These people will be visited during 1988. Recommendations from other areas will only be considered during December 1988 because of the complexities of re-settling married couples, siblings residing together and others who may require psychiatric counselling.

LIST FOR USE WITH TASK 7

PILOT LIST - SPECIALLY ADAPTED ACCOMMODATION

Mrs M Bickerstaffe	59	Area B	HAR
Mr & Mrs P James		Area D	HAR
Mr K Preston	76	Area D	HAR
Mrs V Makin	53	Area D	HAR
Mr T Appleton	56	Area C	HAR
Miss L Anders	65	Area A	HAR
Mr J Johnson	54	Area D	HAR
Mr V Corns	73	Area B	HAR
Misses Fillingham		Area D	LAR
Mr & Mrs Graham		Area D	LAR
Mr F Hathaway	71	Area D	LAR
Mrs K Armson	83	Area D	LAR
Mr & Mrs Bettridge		Area D	LAR
Mr & Mrs Vesty		Area D	LAR
Mrs J Carrington	69	Area B	LAR
Mr R Hinchcliffe	69	Area B	LAR
Mr P Twist	71	Area D	LAR
Mr & Mrs Kay		Area D	LAR
Mr J Mason	87	Area D	LAR
Mrs K Johnson	65	Area A	LAR
Mr P Arthur	66	Area A	LAR
Mrs A Andrews	63	Area A	LAR
Miss L Barton	82	Area A	SSR
Mr & Mrs Beswick		Area D	SSR
Mrs J Carruthers	84	Area A	SSR
Mr & Mrs Carter		Area D	SSR
Mrs L Harrison	58	Area A	SSR
Mrs K Baxter	47	Area C	SSR
Mr & Mrs Dimmock		Area D	SSR
Mr & Mrs Robinson		Area D	SSR
Mr T Darbyshire	79	Area A	SSR
Miss S Dean	80	Area A	SSR
Mr & Mrs Eaves		Area D	SSR
Mr P Evans	71	Area C	SSR
Mr & Mrs Farrelly		Area D	SSR
Mrs B Forshaw	63	Area D	SSR
Mr B Jones	78	Area D	SSR

These people will be visited during September 1988.

Worked examples

1 Letters and memos

Task 1.1

PRAXITELES GROUP

A fictitious organisation for examination purposes only

PRAXITELES HOUSE · ADAM STREET · LONDON WC2N 6EZ
TELEPHONE 01 930 5115

Our ref SO/4/HP

Your ref

(Date of typing)

CONFIDENTIAL

Mr S Quinton
West Wing
Beech House
Church Lane
SOUTH OCKENDEN
Essex RM15 4EJ

Dear Mr Quinton

Following my recent visit to discuss your present plans, I now advise you
that, on receipt of your authorisation, work could start on Thursday of
next week, (Date appropriate to date of typing) and would be completed in
time for your wife's birthday, ie within two weeks of commencement.

   As discussed with you, the "Domed Regent" summer chalet will be
   erected at the site marked on the enclosed sketch map. A firm
   concrete base will first be laid, topped with quarry tiles and
   having two curved, shallow steps to the lawn. A shaped pond,
   approximately 2 m x 4 m with a maximum depth of 60 cm and having
   a yorkstone paved surround, will also be made as shown on the
   sketch map.

As requested by you, I enclose an extra copy of this letter (together with an
additional copy of the map) for your co-owner, Mr Shaw.

My company has plenty of experience in projects of this nature. I can assure
you that the necessary work will be carried out with as little inconvenience
as possible by a group of responsible workers.

I look forward to hearing from you within the next few days.

Yours sincerely
PRAXITELES LANDSCAPES PLC

H Phoenix
Director

Encs

Copy to: <u>Mr Shaw</u>   (carbon copy)

Copy to: Mr Shaw   (second carbon copy)

M E M O R A N D U M

From H Phoenix   *Ref* SO/4

To M Patel   *Date* (Date of typing)

PROPOSED WORK AT BEECH HOUSE, SOUTH OCKENDEN

I have today written to Mr Quinton confirming that this work could
be put in hand immediately. (This project is apparently a surprise
birthday gift for his wife and I have made a definite promise to
start as soon as we receive his confirmation and to complete in two
weeks.) The work has also been agreed with the co-owner, Mr Shaw.

In the meantime, please check with the manufacturer that the chalet
will be delivered here during next week. This was discussed with
their salesman yesterday.

Please detail the quantities of materials needed and check there is
sufficient in stock. I have ordered 12 shrubs, 36 alpines and 40
water plants.

The best team would be George (who has worked at Beech House
before), Tom and Ali. Perhaps you could check their schedules then
let me know if there are any difficulties.

(carbon copy)

PRAXITELES GROUP

A fictitious organisation for examination purposes only

PRAXITELES HOUSE · ADAM STREET · LONDON WC2N 6EZ
TELEPHONE 01 930 5115

Our ref   MW/JK/1

Your ref

(Date of typing)

Mr F Latham
2 Queens Drive
Manchester
M24 4EQ

Dear Mr Latham

LEATHER COAT

I have now had an opportunity to consider the report received from our
laboratory about your leather coat.

It is necessary to follow special procedures when cleaning such coats and
our manager was correct to estimate 3 weeks. The company therefore
accepts that you should not have had to wait for your coat for 7 weeks.

With regard to your complaint about the quality of cleaning, I feel that
the manager was justified in asking you to pay £12 for the extra cleaning to
remove stubborn stains. Our guarantee covers normal soiling only and your
coat was heavily soiled down the front. In addition, the laboratory's
report includes the following wording:

> "It is clear that solvents were used prior to specialised
> cleaning and this has left rubbed and faded patches down
> the front of the coat. This is against the advice of the
> manufacturers. Dirty marks on left sleeve are paint marks and
> will not come out."

In view of the fact that your coat was kept for too long a time, the
company is willing to offer a reduction of £5. This will compensate for the
inconvenience suffered by you. I cannot accept responsibility for the
damage caused by solvents.

I look forward to hearing from you.

Yours sincerely

M Winston
Director

(Carbon copy)

MEMORANDUM

From M Winston, Director   *Ref* MW/JK/1

To   E Hayes, Branch Manager (Manchester)   *Date* (Date of typing)

CONFIDENTIAL

I enclose a laboratory report on the leather coat from your branch. They
believe we are not to blame for faulty cleaning but in future there must
always be enough staff on duty to avoid delays.

I shall be in the north west on Thursday and Friday of next week to see
Janet Baines and I am sending her a copy of this memo to remind her of our
meeting at 2 pm on Thursday (Date appropriate to date of typing). We could
all have dinner that evening at 7.30 pm if you are agreeable. We could
then discuss fully the problems we are having with leather and sheepskin
cleaning. Obviously staff are not taking enough care and it may mean that
you and Janet will have to consider re-training and/or disciplinary
measures for some. The branch image must not suffer.

Enc

cc: Janet Baines

cc: Janet Baines   (Carbon copy)

cc: Janet Baines   (Second carbon copy)

Task 1.3

PRAXITELES GROUP

A fictitious organisation for examination purposes only

PRAXITELES HOUSE · ADAM STREET · LONDON WC2N 6EZ
TELEPHONE 01 930 5115

Our ref PGC/SS

Your ref

(Date of typing)

The Manager
Woodbridge Hotel
Wallman Street
IPSWICH
Suffolk
IP2 3GW

Dear Sir

PRAXITELES GROUP CONFERENCE

An unexpected problem has arisen in connection with my company's
conference, due to be held at your hotel in a fortnight's time.
One of our main speakers, Mr Alec Jones, due to be present for the
whole 4 days, has been involved in an accident and now needs to
bring with him his wife and daughters, aged 10 and 12. I presume
it will be possible for Mr and Mrs Jones to share a double room.
Are you able also to offer accommodation to the 2 young girls
preferably in a room with 2 beds? Mrs Jones and the children
will also require breakfast and evening meals. Meals will be
taken with the conference delegates. If this is possible, please
advise me immediately. I am sending a copy of this letter to
Mr Jones, who will be personally responsible for the extra
expense involved and should be invoiced accordingly.

I confirm that the total number of "live-in" delegates, including
Mr Jones, remains at 26. In addition, there will be 8 daily
visitors, needing morning and afternoon drinks and lunch on each
day of the conference.

    All other arrangements, use of rooms and facilities
    etc, remain as agreed with you.

A copy of our conference catalogue is now enclosed. May I take
this opportunity to thank you for your help in the past, and hope
that this late change will not prove inconvenient. As arranged, I
will call to see you between 14.30 and 15.00 hours on Friday of
next week (date appropriate to date of typing).

Yours faithfully

Conference Secretary

Enc
cc: Mr Jones

cc: <u>Mr Jones</u>   (Carbon copy)

cc: Mr Jones   (Second carbon copy)

M E M O R A N D U M

From Sheila Suzman   *Ref* SS/218

To Alec Jones   *Date* (Date of typing)

<u>PERSONAL</u>

<u>Praxiteles Group Conference</u>

Enclosed is a copy of a letter which has today been sent to the
Woodbridge Hotel. I do not anticipate any difficulties regarding
the accommodation of your wife and daughters.

We greatly appreciate your decision to attend the conference despite
the accident and the Accountant has therefore been instructed to make
an ex gratia payment to cover your family's hotel expenses. Please
send him a photocopy of the receipted account in due course.

I wish you a full and speedy recovery.

Enc

(carbon copy)

Task 1.4

PRAXITELES GROUP

A fictitious organisation for examination purposes only

PRAXITELES HOUSE · ADAM STREET · LONDON WC2N 6EZ
TELEPHONE 01 930 5115

Our ref   F4.3.2

Your ref

PERSONAL   (Date of typing)

Mrs D Williams
3 Rutland Crescent
WARRINGTON
WA1 3EY

Dear Mrs Williams

THE OWLS NEST, WARRINGTON

As requested, I enclose our estimate for the fittings you are considering for
your new accommodation.

These fittings have been chosen from the point of view of their providing:

a) a clear sweep of working surfaces

b) hygienically sealed work tops

c) adequate storage space.

The designs have been chosen in order to give efficient food production where
speed, cleanliness and the minimum of expense are important. The prices quoted
are competitive and we have allowed for expansion as your business grows.

Our usual terms will apply, ie a trade discount of 5%, and a cash discount of
10% if the account is settled within 28 days.

Mr Appleton, our regional sales manager, will be in your area on Wednesday,
(date appropriate to date of typing) and I am sending him a copy of this letter
so that he can arrange to call and see you. I hope by that time you and your
partner will be able to give him a decision.

If there is any way in which I can help you, please do not hesitate to contact
me.

Yours sincerely

John Millward
Manager

cc: Mr Appleton

Enc

cc: Mr Appleton   (Carbon copy)

cc: Mr Appleton   (Second carbon copy)

MEMORANDUM

From   John Millward, Manager   *Ref*   FW.3.1

To   Ronald Appleton,   *Date* (Date of typing)
         Regional Sales Manager

I am enclosing a copy of a letter I have sent to Mrs D Williams of Warrington.

I received an enquiry from her for miscellaneous fixtures and fittings for the

new restaurant she is opening in approximately 3 months.

I will not have an opportunity to see her because of my commitments. I thought

that you could give her some advice on the following lines.

        Other manufacturers do not offer the range of colours
        that we offer – this is most important! Our joiners
        are highly trained craftsmen who are able to fit
        awkward areas to the best advantage.

Please call to see me when you are here on Friday. I am free between 10 am and

11 am and again 3 pm to 4 pm. It would appear that concern is being expressed

about the decreasing number of 'domestic' kitchens we are fitting. High

interest rates, do you think? Or is there some other reason?

Enc

                                           (Carbon copy)

Note: it is not possible to type 'John Millward, Manager' on 2 lines here without infringing Syllabus Objective C.9. The comma (or 2 spaces) is therefore essential here but does not commit the typist to full punctuation style for the whole memo.

MEMORANDUM

From   Lynn Marsh, Personnel Officer   *Ref*   R28946

To   Eden Poulet, Fieldwork Section   *Date*   (Date of typing)

Of the 6 candidates interviewed for the 2 clerical posts for Fieldwork Section, 4 would definitely be suitable for employment here. I have therefore chosen those most fitted for your section and retained the other 2 names on our books (though at this stage with no guarantee of jobs). The following have been offered employment with you.

       MR RICHARD PHILPOT, aged 18, a post 'A' level school leaver whose home is in Kent.

       MISS MARIE MANUEL, aged 21, currently a junior clerk with a rival finance company, who lives in Essex.

The appointments will take effect from the beginning of next month. Both candidates have been asked to report direct to you.

I am sending a copy of this memo to the Training Officer, since induction and training of these new clerks will take place as soon as he is able to arrange it. The Training Officer will notify you when a suitable opportunity arises.

I believe both these young people will settle well and work effectively, but please let me know immediately if there are any problems.

cc Training Officer

cc <u>Training Officer</u>   (carbon copy)

cc Training Officer   (second carbon copy)

PRAXITELES GROUP

A fictitious organisation for examination purposes only

PRAXITELES HOUSE · ADAM STREET · LONDON WC2N 6EZ
TELEPHONE 01 930 5115

Our ref R28946/LM

Your ref

(Date of typing)

PERSONAL

Mr Richard Philpot
82 Dunbar Street
ORPINGTON   Kent
BR5 8CF

Dear Mr Philpot

APPOINTMENT OF CLERICAL OFFICER

Following your recent interview, I am pleased to offer you the post of Grade 3 Clerical Officer in the Fieldwork Section of this company.

Your appointment will take effect from Monday (Date appropriate to date of typing) and you should report at 0900 hours to Mr Poulet in Fieldwork Section on the 4th floor of this building.

You are required to work a minimum of 35 hours per week. The company operates a flexitime system but you must be at work between 1000 hours and 1600 hours. You will be entitled to 24 days' leave each year. Your commencing salary will be at scale point 2 on Grade 3. A list of salary scales is in the introductory booklet enclosed with this letter.

Your appointment is subject to the satisfactory completion of the enclosed medical statement and if necessary you will be required to undergo a medical examination.

We hope you will develop and enjoy your career with us.

Yours sincerely

Mrs Lynn Marsh, Personnel Officer

Encs

(carbon copy)

Task 1.6

PRAXITELES GROUP

A fictitious organisation for examination purposes only

PRAXITELES HOUSE · ADAM STREET · LONDON WC2N 6EZ
TELEPHONE 01 930 5115

Our ref   M183.4

Your ref   JFS/PB

(Date of typing)

CONFIDENTIAL

Mr J F Slaid
Adelphi Engineering
Sussex Road
LONDON   WC2N 3AB

Dear James

Thank you for your letter of yesterday's date. I suggest we
meet for lunch on Thursday of next week (Date appropriate to
date of typing) at 1230 hours followed by a formal meeting here
at approximately 1400 hours. May I say that I share your hope
that we can reach a definite agreement on future supplies of raw
materials being ordered jointly by our two firms.

My partners agree that both companies ordering together would be
better able to reap the benefit of larger discounts that bulk
buying will produce. As we are, so to speak, next-door neighbours
there should be few problems with breaking bulk and onward delivery.

I am sending a copy of this letter to Damon Sangay, my Chief
Buyer, as I have asked him to be present at our discussions after
lunch. His previous experience with co-operative buying should
prove invaluable in our deliberations.

I look forward to a profitable meeting.

Yours sincerely

H Romano
Managing Director

cc <u>Mr D Sangay</u>   (carbon copy)

cc Mr D Sangay   (second carbon copy)

MEMORANDUM

From Henry Romano		*Ref* AE/HR	
To Damon Sangay		*Date* (Date of typing)	

<u>Joint Buying - Adelphi Engineering</u>

I enclose a copy of my letter to James Slaid, Director of
Adelphi Engineering, with whom negotiations have now been
opened to decide the feasibility of joint bulk buying of
raw materials. As stated in the letter, I should like you
to be present at next week's meeting, which will start at
1400 hours. In the meantime would you consider the following
points.

  If a monthly order of, say, £5,000 were placed with the
  manufacturer would the discounts (now 2%, then 5%)
  outweigh the expense of breaking bulk and onward
  delivery?

  What specific problems would be likely in regard to
  delivery, storage, etc, and how could they be successfully overcome?

  Can you recommend a reliable division of responsibility
  for orders, particularly in the case of faulty goods
  being received, delayed delivery or other problems?

It might be a good idea for us to talk prior to the meeting
at, say, 1000 hours in my office on that Thursday. Please
let me know if this is inconvenient for you.

I need hardly say that I greatly value your help and initiative
in this matter.

Enc

(carbon copy)

2 Postcards

Task 2.1

PRAXITELES GROUP

A fictitious organisation for examination purposes only

Praxiteles House · Adam Street · London WC2N 6EZ · Telephone: 01-930 5115

(Date of typing)

Thank you for your reminder about the Personal Computer Club's Annual General Meeting. I am happy to confirm that I am looking forward to the event and I shall be able to attend for the whole evening. As I have a late afternoon meeting here, I shall come straight from the office and expect to arrive at Ilford Station at 1905 hours. I would appreciate it if someone could meet me there. If this is not possible, I will of course pick up a taxi.

Mrs Doreen Foster
19 Western Approach
Seven Kings
ILFORD Essex
IG8 4BT

Task 2.2

PRAXITELES GROUP

A fictitious organisation for examination purposes only

Praxiteles House · Adam Street · London WC2N 6EZ · Telephone: 01-930 5115

(Date of typing)

We regret to inform you that "The Retaliation of Edwina - Volume 3: The Matriarch of Dalgety Minories" ordered on 14 October last is out of print. The publishers inform us that a reprinting will commence on the 1st of next month. Copies should be available within 8 weeks from then. Please inform us if you wish to cancel the order in which event your deposit of £2.00 will be refunded.

Mr B Sheldon
10 Regency Road
Harborne
BIRMINGHAM
B17 12QQ

Task 2.3

PRAXITELES GROUP

A fictitious organisation for examination purposes only

Praxiteles House · Adam Street · London WC2N 6EZ · Telephone: 01-930 5115

Thank you for your enquiry regarding the refurbishment of your offices. Our representative, Mr John Beeston, will be visiting your area in the next few weeks. He could call on you to consider your exact requirements and would bring with him samples of colours, finishes, etc. He will also be able to tell you about our brand new furniture range (not yet in the catalogue) and our special discount offers. Please telephone Mr Beeston on 01 930 5115 Extension 128 to make a definite appointment. He will be expecting your call.

```
The Office Administrator
Beauchamp, Hethersett & Sons PLC
5th Floor Homerton House
Ward Business Park
Thurrock Road
CHELMSFORD
Essex   CM1 3AB
```

Task 2.4

PRAXITELES GROUP

A fictitious organisation for examination purposes only

Praxiteles House · Adam Street · London WC2N 6EZ · Telephone: 01-930 5115

```
Praxiteles Records
Classical Music Department

(Date of typing)

Rossini: The Barber of Seville
```

We have pleasure in advising you that the above recording which you asked us to order on your behalf is now in stock and will be held for you for 10 days subsequent to which it will be added to our sales stocks if not collected by you. The price is £22.99. Please quote R/SHE/1288 in any communication.

```
Mr Martin Bell
37 Oakland Drive
Edgbaston
BIRMINGHAM
B16 4LW
```

Task 2.5

PRAXITELES GROUP

A fictitious organisation for examination purposes only

Praxiteles House · Adam Street · London WC2N 6EZ · Telephone: 01-930 5115

(Date of typing)

Thank you for your telephone enquiry for our kitchen service. Our local surveyor, Mr Colin Westmorland, will call in the next few days to draw up a scale plan to your exact requirements and arrange a convenient commencing date. Please telephone him on 0278 63910 for a definite appointment. Meanwhile, you may like to visit your nearest local showroom at Leatherhead to view our extensive range of cabinets and appliances.

Mrs M Edmunds
28 Camberley Drive
REIGATE
Surrey
RH2 8BW

Task 2.6

PRAXITELES GROUP

A fictitious organisation for examination purposes only

Praxiteles House · Adam Street · London WC2N 6EZ · Telephone: 01-930 5115

(Date of typing)

We have now completed the list for the Harringdon Green Up Scheme and you are part of the team that will tackle Mason Hall corner. Please let me know if you are interested in being Committee Chairperson in the next session - I should be grateful if you could get back to me as soon as possible on this. Contact me on my home telephone number which is 0202 683090.

MRD

Barbara Morris
3 The Limes
Oakwood
Harringdon
BOURNEMOUTH
Dorset
BH62 4QP

3 Typed drafts for correction

Task 3.1

PRAXITILE PRODUCTS LTD

Over the past few months we have been reassessing the design concepts
of our products. Extensive market research has been carried out with
householders in all parts of the country. This has confirmed the
suspicion that our tile designs are lagging behind the times, and that
drastic measures must be taken in order to bring ourselves back into
line with current trends.

The following tile products should definitely be redesigned.

(1) Ceramic wall tiles

These tiles are suitable for use in kitchens and bathrooms. An
attractive fruit and flowers design in a variety of colour combinations has been selected for kitchens, with matching plain tiles to
provide for greater flexibility of layout. For the bathroom we have
chosen a simple, three-colour yacht design (red, yellow and orange
are the colours we recommend). A wavy blue sea motif is chosen for
the accompanying plain tiles which, like the kitchen version, may be
used in varying combinations with the yacht design. The motif tiles
will be sold in packs of ten, and the plain tiles in packs of twenty.

(2) Self-adhesive floor tiles

This is a product line which has been steadily growing in popularity.
A number of different designs have been selected, which should provide
an attractive choice of styles. The following product names have been
suggested, and are to be finalised once market research results have
been received.

(a) Italian Renaissance
(b) Celtic
(c) Gothic
(d) Georgian
(e) Victorian
(f) Edwardian

A new, hard-wearing plastic has recently been developed. This is
virtually unbreakable, and will soon be introduced into the manufacture of these new floor tiles. They will be self-adhesive, with a

- 2 -

peel-off backing, which will facilitate cutting into shape if necessary
before laying. They will be sold in packs of ten.

(3) Polystyrene ceiling tiles

Instead of the completely plain surface of our present tiles, the new
version will have a raised pattern. Up to six designs are planned.
As in the case of the floor tiles, we believe they will be sold in
packs of ten. A special glue is being obtained from a top manufacturer, to be given away with quantity purchases as part of a promotional
campaign.

(4) Marketing strategy

We are now compiling a comprehensive book of samples for sales staff
to show to suppliers. There will also be a brief questionnaire for
completion. In addition to these activities, a promotional exhibition
evening is planned, to which all our major clients will be invited.

ALL SALES AND MARKETING STAFF WILL BE ASKED TO ATTEND A BRIEFING
MEETING ON THIS MATTER VERY SHORTLY. PLEASE CHECK THE NOTICE BOARDS
REGULARLY FOR FURTHER DETAILS.

Task 3.2

HOUSE HUNTING? You are in need of something larger or perhaps it is
your first. Whichever it is, you will probably need to raise a substantial loan. A house will normally be the most expensive
commodity you will ever buy, with a car definitely coming second.

There are some necessary constraints which you must consider when deciding
on the house you like. You must obviously be able to afford the purchase
price, but you are also responsible for such things as maintenance.
Once you are satisfied that you can fulfil these points, you can
make an offer to the seller. You should also advise your solicitor. He
will confirm the offer. If this is accepted, you must complete a loan
application. The lender will then arrange for a company to survey the
property and, if successful, you will receive an offer of loan.

S O U R C E S   O F   M O R T G A G E   F U N D S

1 Building Societies

As a rule, building societies may be prepared to lend between 2½ and 3 times
your annual income. This will not normally be more than 95% of the
surveyor's valuation of the property or the purchase price, whichever is
the lower. Some building societies have been known to consider percentages
over 95%, but this depends to a large extent on the type of property and
the particular building society involved. In addition, they will usually
take into account both incomes of joint borrowers, or at least a proportion
of the lower.

2 Banks and Other Lenders

Many lenders now provide funds on a similar basis to building societies.
Their lending requirements will sometimes differ from a building society,
usually in the minimum amount they will lend. You need to find out as soon
as you start house hunting the maximum amount you will be allowed to borrow.
Some lenders now provide you with a certificate which confirms your borrowing
level.

2

You should take great care in choosing your building society or other
lender and find the one whose terms and conditions suit your requirements.

3 Savings

No matter how much capital you need to borrow, you will be required to pay
a deposit for your property. You should, therefore, start a savings account
with a bank or building society as soon as possible. This will not only
help to accumulate money for your deposit, but will also improve your
prospects of obtaining a mortgage.

Finally, on the lighter side, when you have bought your house, you will
need to advise the following that you are moving

1 job related: employers, tax office

2 home based services: electricity and gas suppliers, milkman, newsagent,
   district council

3 personal services: bank, doctor, dentist, insurance and credit card
   companies.

Task 3.3

LEGAL AID - IS THERE ANY JUSTICE?

G E N E R A L   N O T E S   F O R   A P P L I C A N T S

At some time in your life you are likely to need the services of a solicitor. This may be for a conveyancing matter, making a will, or even a court case. You may be entitled to legal aid. This is a Government scheme covering the payment (or a proportion) of your solicitor's bill. Whether you pay anything depends on your financial circumstances, ie:

(a) your income
(b) your marital status
(c) your husband's/wife's income, if any
(d) if you have children
(e) if you receive Supplementary Benefit.

Emergencies

You can apply for emergency legal aid. This lasts only until a decision has been taken on your full application. However, you must agree:

(a) to co-operate in any enquiry into your financial position
(b) to pay any contribution that is decided
(c) to pay the full cost of your case if it is found that you do not qualify for legal aid.

If your application is refused, you will receive a notice giving you an explanation. You can appeal against a refusal for legal reasons although not if the Department of Social Security states that you are above the financial limit. You should be told if you are entitled to appeal.

It costs nothing to ask for information on legal aid. This can be from a solicitor, a Citizens Advice Bureau, County or Magistrates' Court or a Public Library. If your earnings or savings are too high then you will not qualify. It helps only those who can least afford to pay for the

---

2

help they need. No matter how little money you have, everyone should have equal access to justice. Without this scheme, it would cost more public money. There would be more children in care, more people held in custody, or more Social Security benefits for those unable to be awarded compensation for accidents.

What Happens If You Win (Or Lose)?

If you win, the amount you will have to pay your solicitor will depend on whether the other side is ordered to pay your costs and whether you are awarded anything. You may be paid back some, or all, of any contribution you paid. When your solicitor's costs have been assessed, the balance is paid to you.

If you lose your case, you will have to pay the maximum contribution which will have been worked out when you made the application.

Application Forms

These are obtainable from your local office of the Department of Social Security. Complete and return your form as soon as possible.

Task 3.4

P R A X I   B O O K S H O P S   L T D

PROGRESS REPORT

We have had a successful year on the whole, with a number of interesting developments. These have included:

(a) the purchase of new premises

(b) special signings by celebrity authors

(c) cut-price books

(d) cards and stationery

and further details on these are given below.

New Premises

The number of bookshops has increased from 20 to 35 during the past year. Premises have been purchased in cities such as Leeds, Bristol and Manchester, as well as in large towns and suburbs of London. This has, of course, led to a dramatic increase in the number of employees. Managers have been recruited for all our new shops, as well as sales staff, both full time and part time. Further acquisitions are envisaged for the coming year, and for the first time we are extending our territory into Scotland and Wales.

Celebrity Signings

These have taken place in Central London and in Liverpool. Nine authors in total have spent a busy afternoon talking to customers and signing copies of their recently published books. They have included:

(1) Cranford Drumble - _Little Old Ladies_

(2) Susan Eliot - _Cooking For Your Freezer_

(3) Richard Norris - _Diary Notes_

(4) Johnny Jones - _Going Home_

- 2 -

(5) Anita Glossop - _Derbyshire in Winter_

Bargain Books

These are high-quality remaindered books, always popular as Christmas and birthday presents. They are displayed near the entrance to each shop, and have been found to attract more customers, not just to the Bargain Books section itself, but into all areas of the shop. We estimate that this should increase turnover and profits by up to 30 per cent, thereby making it possible to expand our business throughout the country.

Greetings Cards and Stationery

This has been an important addition to our business. Customers come into a shop for a specific purpose, and then stay longer to browse. This can often lead to the purchase of at least one book, as well as the item initially sought.

We have found it best to position this section towards the rear of the shop, so that customers have to pass rows of attractively presented books on their way in and out. At the same time, a window display makes it clear to passers-by that cards and stationery are available.

Because of such rapid expansion, we feel it is now time to hold a bookshop managers' meeting. This is to take place within the next

- 3 -

few months, and will be designed so that all managers can meet and compare notes. Company Directors will also attend.

HOW TO BECOME THE EXPERT HOME DECORATOR

The information in this article includes guidance on how to calculate quantities of materials, suggestions on tools you will need, and a brief explanation on how to paint.

Painting is a relatively easy task, but it is important to plan the work to be undertaken. You need to spend time on preparing the surface properly before you start painting. If possible paint in good daylight.

It is definitely a good idea to decide on an order of painting, eg:

1 CEILINGS   4 WINDOWS
2 WALLS   5 RADIATORS
3 DOORS   6 SKIRTING BOARDS.

<u>Calculating the quantity of paint you will need</u>

To work out how much paint you will need to paint a room, measure the length of each surface and multiply by the height. This will give you the area in square metres. For emulsion - add all the wall and ceiling areas together to calculate the total surface area; for gloss - add all the metal and woodwork areas together. Any Do-It-Yourself store will help you work out the quantities.

<u>Tools you are likely to need</u>

Having the right tool for the right job will save time and effort. After completion, tools should be thoroughly cleaned; then they will stay in good condition for longer. In order to do a professional job, you will need the following, although should your budget not allow you to purchase everything we recommend, then you must exercise your own judgement.

(a) Bucket, sponge, sugar soap, brush, stripper, step-ladder and dust sheets. It is necessary to wash paintwork and remove dust; a blow torch or liquid paint stripper is quick and efficient. Plastic sheets are better than newspapers for dust sheets, to avoid paint or water soaking through.

(b) Various grades of sandpapers and different size scrapers. A wooden block is useful to hold the paper firmly. Wet-and-dry paper is excellent to achieve a smooth surface.

(c) Filler, filling knives and masking tape. Cracks have to be made good and masking tape is used to protect areas and edges not to be painted.

2

(d) Paint pad or roller, paint tray and brushes, depending on your preference. Paint pads or rollers are good for applying emulsion to larger areas. Brushes are necessary for finishing off and for applying gloss.

<u>How to apply gloss or emulsion paints</u>

Make sure the brushes are clean and dry as well as the surfaces to be painted. Dip up to one-third of the bristles in the paint. Hold the brush like a pen and if you are using gloss paint, do not brush out too thinly. Emulsion paint should be worked in with random strokes to cover evenly.

H A P P Y   D E C O R A T I N G

4 Forms and straight-line diagrams

Task 4.1

PRAXI GLASS PLC

It will be necessary because of the building of the new office
block and canteen to mark out a new parking ground for staff. This
will be where the old warehouse was and the police are insistent
that there should be no parking in the side streets which surround
this area. Special parking is to be made available for employees
who have a disabled sticker.

You are asked to fill in and return the slip below so that a
suitable space can be allocated to you. Before a special disc can
be issued to staff, staff will be asked to produce an owner's
registration document and a valid tax certificate.

Once the building is finished and the workmen have moved their
huts, there will be only a limited amount of space on the old site.
This will be left clear for access by fire vehicles and ambulances.

....

PRAXI GLASS PLC

Surname

Forename(s)

Address

Department

Position in the company

Telephone extension

Make of car   Registration

PRAXI GLASS PLC

P R O P O S E D   P A R K I N G   A R E A S

Staff will be issued with coloured stickers which must be displayed on the
car windscreen. STAFF WILL BE DENIED ENTRY IF THE STICKER IS NOT CLEARLY
VISIBLE.

AREA A Directors and senior management	Exit only AREA A Employees with disabled stickers

Church
Road   Entry only   Entry only   Birch
Road

AREA B
Visitors only

AREA B
Administration
staff

Entry only   Entry only

AREA C
Maintenance
staff

AREA C
Factory staff

Exit
only

COLOURS OF STICKERS

Area A left – blue

Area A right – red

Area B left – yellow

Area B right – green

Area C left – brown

Area C right – orange

Area C only will be manned between the hours of 6 pm and 7 am. Staff working
late are asked to make special arrangements with security staff for a night pass
to be issued.

Task 4.2

Dear

Due to the recent expansion of the company's business, it has
been decided to hold a conference of bookshop managers. This
should be taking place within the next four months and, if it
proves successful, is likely to become an annual event.

It is envisaged that the conference will be scheduled over two
full days. The venue will be an hotel in the East Midlands.

Please complete the tear-off slip below and return it
to our head office by the end of the week. Further
details will be sent to you as soon as the dates and
a suitable venue have been confirmed.

Yours sincerely

Eric Winterton
Director
PRAXI BOOKSHOPS LTD
....

NAME ....

BOOKSHOP ADDRESS ....

HOME ADDRESS ....

BUSINESS TELEPHONE NUMBER ....

HOME TELEPHONE NUMBER ....

SUGGESTION(S) FOR AGENDA ....

....

DATES NOT AVAILABLE (DUE TO HOLIDAYS ETC) OVER NEXT FOUR MONTHS

....

DATE OF JOINING COMPANY ....

P R A X I   B O O K S H O P S   L T D

SUGGESTED BOOKSHOP LAYOUT

It has been found through recent discussions that the following
floor layout has resulted in higher sales. Bearing in mind that
not all floor areas are identical in shape, please try to adhere
as closely as possible to this layout.

```
+---------------------------------------------------+
|                REAR OF PREMISES                   |
|  +------------+              +----------------+    |
|  | STATIONERY |              | GREETINGS CARDS|    |
|  +------------+              +----------------+    |
|                                                   |
|                                                   |
|   PLEASE ARRANGE                                  |
|   OTHER CATEGORIES                                |
|   AS YOU SEE FIT.                                 |
|                                                   |
|                                                   |
|   +------+      +---------+       +------+        |
|   | TILL |      | BARGAIN |       | TILL |        |
|   +------+      |  BOOKS  |       +------+        |
|                 +---------+                        |
|                FRONT OF PREMISES                   |
|                (ENTRANCE AND EXIT)                 |
+---------------------------------------------------+
```

In shops where there are
both front and rear doors,
at least one till, together
with a bargain books table,
should be positioned near
each. Stationery and
greetings cards should be
placed as far away as
possible from the doors.

Any comments on the above layout will be discussed at the
forthcoming bookshop managers' conference.

PRAXI SERIES III

INTRODUCTION

The aim of this book is to assist you to use and understand your Praxi
Series III fitted oven and grill unit.

Please read the instructions with care and always keep the booklet handy
for future reference and guidance.

You have purchased a quality cooker and when looked after it will provide
you with many years of good service. If, however, you should be
unfortunate and have problems, please contact your supplier in the first
instance.

To assist the disabled user in handling the appliance, adaptors are
available to allow you to fit a specially designed tap handle. For the
blind user, oven control knobs marked in braille are available. Please
contact your supplier if you need any of these special aids.

All packaging materials and protective film must be removed before
operating the appliance; please refer to installation and servicing notes.

Please complete the tear off slip below for membership of our users' club.

Surname

Forename(s)

Address

Telephone number

Name of supplier

Address of supplier

Date appliance fitted   Serial number

A stamped addressed envelope must be included with the reply slip.

PRAXI SERIES III

E L E C T R I C A L   F A U L T   F I N D I N G

Before carrying out electrical fault finding, it is necessary to carry out
the electrical system check as laid down in the instructions for Praxi gas
cookers pp 6-9.

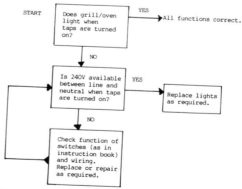

WARNING: DISCONNECT APPLIANCE
FROM ELECTRICITY SUPPLY BEFORE
REMOVING ANY PANELS.

Instruct user and ensure understanding of instructions in user's manual.
Appliances should be fitted by supplier registered with Praxi Gas
Appliances only.

Task 4.4

Dear Retailer

As you may have read in the press, we are in the process of redesigning
our complete range of domestic tile products. This includes ceramic
wall tiles for kitchens and bathrooms, as well as self-adhesive floor
tiles.

I am now writing to invite you to an exhibition of the new designs, to
be held within the next few weeks at our Central London showrooms. The
exhibition will take place from 6pm on a weekday evening and the date
should be confirmed shortly. Refreshments will be provided.

All you need to do is complete the tear-off slip below and return it
to me as soon as possible.

    I AM SURE YOU WILL BE DELIGHTED WITH OUR NEW DESIGNS.

Yours faithfully

Rachel Allen
Marketing Director

....

NAME ....

BUSINESS ADDRESS ....

....

HOME ADDRESS ....

....

BUSINESS TELEPHONE NUMBER ....

HOME TELEPHONE NUMBER ....

AVAILABILITY ....

DATE .... SIGNATURE ....

P R A X I T I L E   P R O D U C T S   L T D

EXHIBITION OF NEW TILE DESIGNS AT CENTRAL LONDON SHOWROOMS

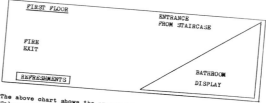

GROUND FLOOR

KITCHEN DISPLAY

REFRESHMENTS

FIRST FLOOR

ENTRANCE FROM STAIRCASE

FIRE EXIT

REFRESHMENTS

BATHROOM DISPLAY

The above chart shows the proposed layout for next week's exhibition.
Sales and Marketing staff are asked to arrive at our Central London
showrooms by 5pm, ready to welcome guests from 6pm onwards. About
one hundred guests are expected, plus a number of directors from our
head office.

A one-page questionnaire is being drawn up, copies
of which will be available at the showroom. Please
make sure that each retailer is provided with one,
for completion and return during the exhibition.

What we learn from our retailers' response to our designs will help
us plan effective sales campaigns.

Task 4.5

(Date of typing)

Dear

PRAXI MEDICAL CENTRE

Everybody concerned with the Praxiteles Group will be pleased to know
that the new centre is nearly complete and will be opened on
                    at

The opening ceremony will be performed by
and will be followed by a lunch held in the Group's John Adam Suite. An
invitation is extended to you and   guests to attend this special
occasion. You are asked to reply no later than
by writing to the above address or by ringing the organiser
(Tel:).

The Praxi Medical Centre will fulfil a need expressed by the Group for many
years. Clearly a company with such a large workforce should not have to
rely on first aid provision only. The opening of the continuous process
factory has meant that the employment of trained medical staff is an
absolute necessity.

The centre will contain everything for the treatment of all save major
accidents. A doctor will attend for 4 hours each day and will be "on call"
after that time. X-ray staff and physiotherapy staff will be on hand to
provide treatment services.

I do hope that you will be able to join us.

Yours sincerely

A Friar
Director

P R A X I   M E D I C A L   C E N T R E

Reception / Records		X-ray / Offices
	CORRIDOR A	
Scrub-up / Recovery		Minor surgery
	CORRIDOR B	
Supplies / Laundry		Physiotherapy

Medical personnel only will
be allowed along corridors
A and B because of infection
and security risks.

All personnel employed at
the centre will be recruited
from staff experienced in
this field and they will not
be drawn from Group
personnel.

Provision will be made for daily consultations and 9 nurses will work a
rotation of shifts to ensure medical cover. One full time and 2 part time
physiotherapists will be employed on shift work.

Task 4.6

Dear

We recently sent you details of a series of concerts that we are
promoting. I am now writing to offer you up to three complimentary
tickets for next week's guitar recital, to be held at the Wigmore
Hall.

Each of these tickets will entitle the holder to a top-price seat
in the stalls, and we shall be delighted to welcome yourself and
your guests to a small reception, to be held in the Green Room
after the concert.

     PLEASE COMPLETE THE TEAR-OFF SLIP BELOW, STATING THE
     NUMBER OF TICKETS YOU REQUIRE. PLEASE ALSO LET US
     KNOW WHETHER YOU AND ANY OF YOUR GUESTS WILL BE
     ATTENDING THE RECEPTION, SO THAT WE MAY PLAN FOR
     CATERING.

Yours sincerely

Emma Strauss
Director
PRAXI CONCERT AGENCY
....

NAME ....

ADDRESS ....

....

DAYTIME TELEPHONE NO .... EVENING TELEPHONE NO ....

NO OF TICKETS REQUIRED .... NO ATTENDING RECEPTION ....

DATE .... SIGNATURE ....

P R A X I   C O N C E R T   A G E N C Y

GUITAR RECITAL AT WIGMORE HALL

The following chart gives the suggested layout for the Green
Room for next week's reception.

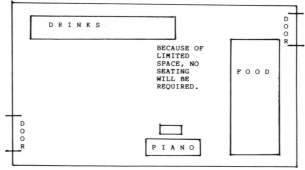

Approximately fifty guests are expected, including music critics
and photographers from the national and local press. Refreshments
are being provided by the Wigmore Hall's catering service, at an
inclusive cost.

Please note that fire regulations in public

buildings must be observed closely.

Smoking should be kept to a minimum.

The concert begins at 8pm. Ticket sales are going well, with just
over one hundred seats left to fill. The reception is scheduled to
start at 9.45pm; the Green Room is available until 11pm.

PRAXI FASHION PARADE

Have you got your tickets yet for the fashion parade of the decade? As
a holder of a Praxi Gold Card and a regular subscriber to our
fashionable magazine you are entitled to a ticket for yourself and one
for a friend.

The parade will be held on Easter Saturday in the ballroom of the PARK
ROYAL HOTEL in London. If you send back the reply slip below, your
name will go into a prize draw. The winners will attend the Parisian
showing of the parade and will be our special guests at the glittering
Louis XIV restaurant. In addition to the fabulous parade you will see
the sights on an accompanied tour of Paris. You can shop for souvenirs
in the fashionable markets and buy luxurious clothes and accessories in
the shops. At night you will take a boat trip down the river and see
sparkling Paris by night.

....

PRAXI FASHION PARADE
NAME ....
ADDRESS ....
....
HOME TEL NO ....
BUSINESS TEL NO ....
CARD NO ....   SUBSCRIPTION NO ....
NAME OF FRIEND ....
ADDRESS ....
....

P R A X I   F A S H I O N   P A R A D E
Look at these famous faces!

Each one of these top
models has agreed to take
part in the fashion
parade of the decade -
the Praxi Fashion
Parade.

As a prelude to the
opening of our new
fashion stores in London
and Paris, we are putt-
ing together a parade of
beautiful clothes
designed specially for
Praxi by the top
designers.

Customers holding a Praxi
Gold Card will be able to
buy these designs with a
generous 10% off the normal
selling price if they can
place their order at the
parade.

The parade itself is set to be an exciting occasion of vibrant colour
and sound. In addition to the famous faces pictured above, we expect
to see many famous names in the audience. The media will also be there
in force to give a boost to British fashion on the world's stage.

Dear Customer

Thank you for your recent letter. I was sorry to hear that the
product you purchased was not entirely to your satisfaction.

Perhaps I should explain that confusion over jar labelling was
the cause of the problem. We are now in the process of redesigning some of our labels, and hope that this will remedy the
situation.

We are sending to you today under separate cover a full refund,
together with a replacement jar of fruit preserve, which we hope
will be to your liking.

**For our records, I wonder if you would be kind enough to complete
the tear-off slip below, and return it to us in the pre-paid
envelope provided.**

Yours faithfully

Samantha Floyd
Public Relations Officer
PRAXI JAMS & PRESERVES LTD

Enc

. . . .

NAME . . . .

ADDRESS . . . .

. . . .

TELEPHONE NUMBER . . . .

PLACE OF PURCHASE . . . .

PURCHASE PRICE . . . .

DESCRIPTION OF PRODUCT . . . .

DATE . . . .

SIGNATURE . . . .

PRAXI JAMS & PRESERVES LTD

N E W   L A B E L   D E S I G N S

Just lately we have been receiving complaints regarding the
contents of our special fruit preserves. This problem seems to
have arisen because labels for jams and for preserves are similar
in appearance, and have been getting confused.

The diagrams below show the updated designs. Name of fruit will
be indicated between asterisks. These labels are being printed at
the moment, and should be ready for use within the next two weeks.

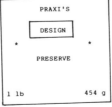

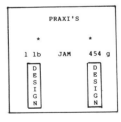

In the meantime, it is most important

that labels for different products are

not confused. Please check all stock,

to ensure that there are no fruit

preserve labels mixed in with those for

jams.

5 Tables

Task 5.1

CLASSICAL RECORDINGS - BASIC STOCK

Opera, Choral and Vocal*

Composer	Work	Price	Record Number
O P E R A			
Beethoven	Fidelio	£23.65	3210-652
Bellini	Puritani	£32.97	7436-543
Bizet	Carmen	£21.97	2347-567
Lehar	Merry Widow	£15.90	3912-094
Mozart	Marriage of Figaro	£33.98	5489-216
Puccini	Boheme	£20.98	7621-890
Rossini	Barber of Seville	£22.97	7120-345
Strauss	Rosenkavalier	£34.95	1235-123
Tchaikovsky	Queen of Spades	£41.99	8341-989
Verdi	Traviata	£32.97	4567-213
C H O R A L			
Allegri	Miserere	£11.99	2342-098
Bach	St Matthew Passion	£34.95	5467-987
Beethoven	Missa Solemnis	£15.99	2312-902
Elgar	Dream of Gerontius	£21.00	2387-097
Handel	Messiah	£22.98	9821-902
Mozart	Requiem	£10.99	1279-769
Verdi	Requiem	£21.50	1234-987
V O C A L			
Berlioz	Nights of Summer	£10.97	5412-043
Brahms	4 Serious Songs	£12.99	3412-034
Elgar	Songs	£13.99	4512-934
Haydn	Songs	£10.50	4519-675
Mozart	Songs	£22.97	2342-012
Schubert	Songs	£12.99	9821-098
Schumann	Liederkreis	£11.50	3256-043
Ravel	Chansons	£23.97	3462-236
Verdi	Songs	£10.97	6542-023

* The above records are to be kept in stock at all times. Should any of them be "out of stock" at the suppliers, consult the Manager of the Music Department. She will advise on other records to stock as a temporary measure. A separate list of records of orchestral, instrumental and chamber music has been compiled. This should be consulted if enquiries for those types of music are received. If in doubt, consult Jean Bastedo, Records Buyer, extension 95.

CAR LEASING FROM NEW LOMBARD CAR LEASING COMPANY

P R A X I T E L E S   G R O U P

(South Western Transport Department)

The following is an up-to-date schedule of the company's commitment for this year. The proposed new contracts will involve cars for all staff at scale 2 and above.

NAME	POSITION	MAKE/MODEL OF VEHICLE	REGISTRATION NO
Construction Division			
G Blackman	General Manager	Ford Granada 2.8 Ghia	E369 ECH
S Brown	Chief Engineer	Ford Sierra 2.0 Ghia	E246 FVP
D Clarke	Works Manager	Ford Sierra 2.0 LX	E247 FVP
F Moore	Contracts Manager	Austin Montego 1.6 L	E698 ORA
H Walsh	Site Engineer	Vauxhall Cavalier 1.8 LI	F123 FMB
J Yelland	Assistant Engineer	Ford Sierra 1.6 L	E248 FVP
Quarries Division			
D Evans	Geologist	Ford Sierra 2.0 LX	E490 FVO
E Perks	Safety Officer	Vauxhall Cavalier 1.6 L	F423 CVB
P Smith	Works Manager	Ford Sierra 2.0 LX	E491 FVO
F Toms	Technical Manager	Opel Manta	F221 HRC
Special Products Division			
L George	Accounts Director	Ford Sierra 2.0 LX	F449 EMO
W Johns	Sales Manager	Austin Maestro 1.6 L	F669 GMB
D Thomas	Works Manager	Austin Montego 1.6 L	E696 ORA
G Westway	Research Manager	Vauxhall Cavalier 1.6 L	F422 CVB
R Williams	Commercial Manager	Vauxhall Carlton 1.8 LI*	F524 EMM

* Awaiting delivery

NB Most cars are now fitted with a radio and cassette. An electronic anti-theft security device is encoded at the time of delivery. Every window is etched with the car's registration number. There is also a security alarm to protect the vehicle. Please ensure that your personnel are made aware of these security measures.

Task 5.2

90

Task 5.3

```
                     P R A X I   B O O K S

        Here is a selection of our best selling fiction and non-fiction
                                 titles

FICTION                          NON-FICTION

Malcolm Arne                     Jodie Baudhury
     Battle Commences                 The Art Of Indian Cooking
     Be My Betrayer                    Indonesian Cuisine*
     Camel Command                     Middle Eastern Cookery
     Cyanide Is A Solution
     Death Before Dishonour       Henry Bagley
     More Than Reason Allows           Better Tennis Strokes*
     Return To New York                Squash Tips For All*
     Revenge Is Sweet
     Ten Little Terrorists       Mary Henley
     Vengeance Extracted               Dried Flower Arrangements
                                       Flower Arranging Made Easy
Gwen Bailey                            The Furniture Of The Garden
     A Dissolute Woman                 The Small Gardener*
     Helen Morgan - A Life
     My Cup Runs Over            Frank Innes
                                       Fitness For The Family*
Betty Brown*                           Get Fit With Frank*
     More Tales Of Tremaine            Workouts For Men And Women*
     The Saga Of Tremaine
     The Tremaine Inheritance    Vashti and Kamlesh Sumra
                                       The Fish Dishes Of Goa
Mary Richards                          Oriental Cookery
     A Better Man Than I
     The More I See You          Henry Thomas
                                       Classical Music Today
Peter Richmond
     Blake's Fall                Paul Vega
     Never Talk To A Stranger         The Popular Music Industry
     Paper Tiger                       Tin Pan Alley

Our latest book catalogue is now in print.  You may collect this
free of charge from all our branches.

Thinking of a gift for a friend?  Our friendly staff will be
happy to gift wrap any purchase free of charge.

* Available in hardback and paperback
```

```
               A D U L T   C O N T I N U I N G   E D U C A T I O N

       District Principal: A Hicks MA    Assistant Principal: B Reid BSc


COLLEGE OF FURTHER EDUCATION (BUSINESS STUDIES) CARETAKER - T HILLMAN

                         Spring Term Courses

Classes commence the second week of January.  If you have difficulty
finding your room, please enquire at the caretaker's office.  This is
situated on the left of the main entrance.

Monday

ROOM NO     COURSE NAME                  TIME

6           Italian for your Holidays    7-9 pm
8           French for your Holidays      7-9 pm
12          Computing - An Introduction   7-9 pm
14          Information Technology        6-8 pm


Tuesday

1           Word Processing RSA I         10-12 noon
2           Typewriting for Beginners     5.30-7 pm
8           Greek Made Simple             6.30-8 pm

Wednesday

1           Word Processing RSA III       7-9 pm
2           Typewriting - Advanced        5.30-7 pm
5           Stockmarket - Continuation*   6.30-8 pm
8           Spanish for your Holidays     7-9 pm
32          Yoga - Over 50s*              10-12 noon

Thursday

1           Word Processing RSA II        7-9 pm
2           Typewriting Retake RSA II     7-9 pm
32          Yoga for Health*              6-8 pm

It would be appreciated if evening class lecturers would switch off all
equipment and lights and close all windows and doors before leaving the
classroom.  The college doors will be locked at 9.30 pm every evening
unless special arrangements are made prior to the evening class.  In
case of an emergency, please ring St Austell 875208.


* subject to room change - check notice board each week.
```

Task 5.4

Task 5.5

```
                              PRAXITELES GROUP

                              Investors' Holdings


Share                    Investor's Name    Holding    Market Value
                                                            £

Barclays Bank            D Ball               250          1,030
                         C Chatsfield         280          1,153
                         J Fox                250          1,030

BAT Industries           D Ball               180            811
                         F Watson             300          1,353

British Gas              C Chatsfield         300            477
                         J Davis              475            756
                         L Thomas             800          1,272

British Telecom          J Davis              435          1,146
                         S Grose              650          1,709

English China Clays      W Corns              320          1,488
                         J Fox                140            651

Hanson Trust             D Ball               600            846
                         C Chatsfield         900          1,269
                         L Thomas             600            846

Land Securities          W Corns              100            548
                         J Fox                230          1,260
                         F Watson             200          1,096

Legal & General          W Corns              300            879

Rolls-Royce              S Grose              390            542
                         F Watson             300            417

TSB Group                J Davis              880            959

                              General Note
```

Under the current rules a PEP investor must be over 18 and resident
in the UK for tax purposes. Only one PEP can be taken out in each
calendar year. The maximum investment is currently £3,000. Provided
that no withdrawals are made from the PEP until the start of the third
year, all income is free from UK taxation. After that time, the PEP
can be retained as a tax-free shelter, but withdrawals can be made
without penalty.

Personal Equity Plans need to be regarded as long-term investments.
They will then accumulate substantial funds which are free from income
tax.

Task 5.6

```
               P R A X I   V I D E O   R E N T A L

                         OUR TOP TEN VIDEOS

Title          Description                    Format      Rental
                                                         per night
                                                            £
"Bird"         The story of jazz saxophonist  VHS only    1.75
               Charlie Parker directed by
               Clint Eastwood

"The Bedroom   Thriller revolving around a    VHS/Beta    1.50
 Window"       false witness

"La Boheme"    Intelligent adaptation of      VHS only    1.50
               Puccini's opera of doomed
               romance

"Buster"       Starring Phil Collins, the     VHS only    1.75
               story of the Great Train
               Robber

"Fatal         The smash hit of 1988, a       VHS/Beta    1.50
 Attraction"   TERRIFYING love story

"A Fish        An hilarious comedy starring   VHS/Beta*   1.75
 called Wanda" John Cleese and Jamie Lee
               Curtis

"Sunset"       A comedy tribute to the        VHS only    1.50
               twilight of the great
               Hollywood silent era

"War Requiem"  A demanding epic of mourning   VHS only    1.50
               for the Great War

"Who framed    The film comedy that combines  VHS only*   1.75
 Roger         live action and cartoon
 Rabbit?"      characters

"Willow"       A fantasy featuring demons,    VHS/Beta    1.75
               dragons and dwarfs
```

If you are not yet a member of Praxi Video Club why not think about
joining?

```
               Life membership    £50.00
               Annual membership   £3.50
```

We also offer an insurance against damage to or loss of video films at
the very reasonable sum of £3.00 per annum.

* These two videos are extremely popular and we recommend that you
  reserve them a week in advance.